**Editor**
Mara Ellen Guckian

**Editor in Chief**
Karen J. Goldfluss, M.S. Ed.

**Illustrator**
Mark Mason

**Creative Director**
Sarah M. Fournier

**Cover Artist**
Sarah Kim

**Imaging**
James Edward Grace
Amanda R. Harter

**Publisher**
Mary D. Smith, M.S. Ed.

D1548254

**GRADE 5**

Teacher Created Resources
TCR 8185

# STEM

## Engaging Hands-On Challenges Using Everyday Materials

**Includes 9 STEM challenges that support Scientific Inquiry and the Engineering Design Process**

**Immerses students in planning, building or investigating, analyzing, and reflecting throughout each challenge**

**Targets Disciplinary Core Ideas, Science and Engineering Practices, and Crosscutting Concepts**

*\* Correlated to NGSS*

Teacher Created Resources

Author
Tracy Edmunds, M.A. Ed.

**Teacher Created Resources**
12621 Western Avenue
Garden Grove, CA 92841
www.teachercreated.com

ISBN: 978-1-4206-8185-7

*© 2018 Teacher Created Resources*
Made in U.S.A.

Teacher Created Resources

# Table of Contents

## Introduction

## Challenges

# Challenges vs. Lessons

The activities in this book are referred to as challenges, not lessons. They are quite different from traditional science lessons that tell students what to do and how to do it. The goal of these challenges is for students to experience phenomena for themselves, which requires a bit of letting go on the part of the teacher. Instead of lecturing or demonstrating, we are putting materials into the hands of students, setting them up for success, and turning them loose to discover new concepts. Teachers are facilitators, laying out the challenges for students, scaffolding when necessary, providing guidance, and checking in with groups to offer encouragement, advice, correction, and support.

Once students understand how the challenges work, they really dive into them. They become fully engaged in working together on their own terms, manipulating materials, and solving a compelling problem or answering an intriguing question, with their hands and minds occupied and on task. And these challenges are not conducive to silence—a low buzz of purposeful conversation indicates that students are actively engaged. Your biggest problem may be getting students to wrap things up!

Students CAN meet the challenge!

Keep in mind that we, as teachers, have to change our approach, too. We tend to want to know what the end product of a challenge should be—a finished product that the students can take home. But inquiry-based lessons in engineering design and the scientific process will naturally go in whatever direction students take them. Give students just enough information and scaffolding, and they will surprise you!

## * Two Kinds of Challenges *

Each challenge is designed for students to experience either the engineering design process or scientific inquiry.

- In the *engineering challenges*, students create a solution to a problem and evaluate the effectiveness of their solutions. They use the engineering design process—*ask, imagine, plan, create (build), test, improve*—to arrive at the best solution they can under the *constraints of the challenge*. Constraints include the rules, limitations, and restrictions students must follow. In these challenges, students must think creatively, meaning that the final solutions will (and should) vary widely—there are no "right" answers. Solutions are evaluated by the class based on how well they solve the given problem.

- For *scientific-inquiry challenges*, scaffolding is provided to give students experience in exploring questions, testing hypotheses, recording data, and evaluating evidence. Although not as student-driven or as open-ended as the engineering challenges, scientific inquiry challenges encourage students to ask questions and create hypotheses (within the parameters of the challenge), so students are deciding what to test and how to test it. Students work with *variables* instead of *constraints* in these challenges. They set up and carry out their planned tests, record and analyze data, and come to their own conclusions, which are then evaluated by the class.

# Standards and Assessments

## ⋆ A Word About Standards ⋆

The Next Generation Science Standards (NGSS) are performance standards that explicitly state what students will do to show proficiency by the end of each grade level. Students must build knowledge and ability toward the performance expectations throughout the school year.

> "As the NGSS are performances meant to be accomplished at the conclusion of instruction, quality instruction will have students engage in several practices throughout instruction."
>
> —NGSS Executive Summary

In every challenge in this book, students will be making sense of phenomena or designing solutions to a problem as they build understanding of science and engineering practices (SEPs), disciplinary core ideas (DCIs), and crosscutting concepts (CCCs). These experiences are designed to lead students toward knowledge, skills, and understanding that they will need to meet the proficiency standards by the end of the grade level.

The science concepts DCIs, CCCs, and SEPs that students will develop and use during their work and reflection are listed at the beginning of each challenge.

## ⋆ Assessment ⋆

As students work through the challenges in this book, teachers should check for understanding through formative assessment in order to get a coherent picture of what students know and can do. To help you formatively assess students' understanding of the ideas, concepts, and practices during each challenge, examine the following evidence:

- Observations of and discussions with students during work time
  (It is recommended that you take notes during these observations.)

- Class sharing and discussions

- Writing Reflection pages

These formative assessments provide multiple sources of evidence to guide you in making inferences about what students understand and are capable of doing and also point toward next steps in instruction. Look specifically for students' understanding of all three dimensions (DCIs, CCCs, and SEPs) and how they work together.

# Meeting the Challenges

## ★ Productive Struggle ★

Inquiry challenges give students a certain amount of freedom, but they should not be free-for-alls. These types of challenges can be overwhelming to students if students aren't provided with enough structure. When you begin these types of inquiry-based activities, you will most likely encounter a lot of "I can't do it" and "Can you help me?" from students. Outside of actual physical incapability (some students really have trouble blowing up balloons), encourage students to try things on their own at least three times and then ask other students for assistance before coming to you. Freedom may be new to some students, and they may be unsure about how to proceed.

Prompt them with the constraints and goals of the challenge, and if they really are stuck, ask leading questions and offer a few choices of next steps they can take.

For example, "I see that your tower is leaning to one side." Then, follow up with questions and suggestions such as:

— Where do you think the weak points might be? How could you make them stronger?

— Maybe you could strengthen the base of your tower. Could you put more spaghetti on that side or add more marshmallows?

Once they get the hang of it, they will stop asking for help and run full speed ahead into each challenge.

## ★ Give Them an Envelope ★

In each Main Challenge, you will set constraints, or rules, that students must follow. The more specific the constraints, the better, and be sure that students understand them. Then, if a student asks if he or she can do something, you can answer, "What do the constraints of this challenge allow?"

Build a very clear envelope for them to work within, and give them complete freedom within it. If students levy a charge of "cheating" at a new idea, have a group discussion about the constraints and whether the new idea falls within them.

## ★ Collaboration ★

Collaboration is a big part of 21st-century learning and STEM (science, technology, engineering, math), but not all students work well together. Flexible grouping is important, as is student choice. If a student requests to work alone, that's perfectly acceptable, as long as he or she participates in a debrief with the class. You will find that even those lone wolves, once they see how much fun the other students are having, will most likely choose to work with others at some point. And if they don't, remember—Einstein and Tesla usually worked alone.

When pairing students or placing them in small groups, allowing them to choose with whom they want to work is often the best option, especially during the first few challenges. The activities are engaging enough that hijinks are rare; students are often too busy to cause trouble.

As students get used to the procedures, you can mix it up and still offer student choice by specifying that everyone must work with someone they haven't worked with before. But always keep an eye on things— forcing students to work with others who make them uncomfortable is counterproductive because social interaction takes their focus off the challenges.

# Meeting the Challenges

## ★ Copying Allowed ★

Let students know that because there are no right answers, copying is allowed! If a group is struggling with a task, one strategy they can employ is to observe the work of others. If students see someone else's great idea, encourage them to use it—with a twist or in a new way to make it their own. Even if they're really stuck and choose to copy another group exactly, they will still have their own experiences. Of course, if a particular student or group copies others in every activity, intervention is warranted.

## ★ Failure Is Always an Option ★

Talk with students about the word *fail*. It has a very different meaning in science and engineering from the one heard in school. Failure is not the end of an experiment or project—it is merely a step along the way. When students are asked to make predictions about what will happen in an experiment, be sure to let them know that it does not matter whether their predictions match what happens. Scientists are wrong in their predictions all the time—it's part of conducting experiments.

**Every failure provides an opportunity for improvement. Scientists and engineers look at why they think something happened and how they can fix or improve it. Then, they try again and again and again.**

I often tell students the story of the *MythBusters* TV show testing whether elephants are afraid of mice (look it up online—the video is great!). They were absolutely sure that this was just a silly tale—why in the world would a giant elephant be afraid of a little mouse? But, lo and behold, the elephants cautiously avoided the mice every time. Were the researchers upset that their prediction did not match the outcome? No! They were astonished and thrilled. *MythBusters'* Adam Savage summed it up: "I'm always pleased to be completely wrong."

## ★ Making Connections ★

We want students to understand why things happen, but instead of telling them, we want them to discover for themselves. At the end of each challenge, bring the class together for a wrap-up session to debrief and analyze their results. This is important—this is where students make connections to internalize scientific processes and engineering concepts.

Students will share and compare their ideas, experiences, data, constructions, and most importantly, evidence. Because it can be difficult for students to let go of their own ideas, they need to practice listening to, comparing, and evaluating competing ideas based on their merits. By looking at data and concrete evidence, e.g., the seeds without soil grew just as tall as the seeds with soil, students build the ability to discern evidence-based fact from opinion.

Bringing the whole class together to share data and observations and analyze outcomes lets us lead students toward discovery and understanding at their level and in their words. They will grasp and remember concepts much better when it comes from them instead of from us.

# Meeting the Challenges

## ★ Materials ★

STEM challenges do not always need specialized tools and equipment. These challenges rely on classroom supplies you probably already have, recycled materials (think paper towel tubes and scratch paper), and sometimes a few items from discount stores. For many of the challenges, the material choices are quite flexible, making it easy to use materials you have available.

Develop specific routines for how students will access materials, and practice with them before each activity. Also, be sure to review safe practices with items like scissors and pushpins. The consequence for not using materials safely should be loss of those materials for the activity in addition to your established classroom consequences.

## ★ Recording ★

> "The only difference between messing around and science is writing it down."
> —Adam Savage of *MythBusters*

Scientists and engineers do a lot of writing in order to turn data into information. Every step of the scientific process is recorded so that other scientists in other places and at other times can replicate experiments. Engineers write procedures, reports, funding requests, and more. And STEM professionals write not only to communicate with others, but also to clarify their thinking, to explore new ideas, and to come to conclusions.

Throughout the challenges in this book, students will be recording their thoughts, ideas, procedures, data, and more on paper. In some cases, they will answer questions that help lead them through an investigation or set them up for success in a challenge. At other times, they will record data as they collect it, and then analyze it to arrive at a conclusion or a result. And in engineering challenges, they will do their planning and evaluating on paper. At the end of each challenge, students will write about their experience by answering reflection questions in order to pull everything together.

Both speaking and writing give students an opportunity to articulate their thinking. As they work on a challenge, they discuss what's going on with other students (yes, you'll find that even students working alone often have discussions with other students). These discussions allow students to work out their thoughts and observations aloud, which makes writing easier. This is particularly helpful for English language learners who practice vocabulary and sentence structure as a natural part of their challenge work time. Encourage students to use their natural language during challenges to communicate their ideas, even if grammar isn't perfect. The same goes for writing—don't worry so much about spelling and punctuation—focus on the ideas.

Drawing is also a big part of recording in these challenges. Visual and symbolic representations such as diagrams, blueprints, technical drawings, schematics, and models are integral parts of science and engineering. In every challenge, students are asked to sketch and label their ideas. Sketching helps students get their ideas on paper quickly and encourages them to think through the relationships of the parts to one another and to the whole. Drawings are similarly great for assessment, as you can see how well students understood the challenge concepts by how they represent those concepts visually.

# Budgets

In all challenges, constraints are specified or, at least, outlined. An extra constraint you can add is a budget. This will force students to be thoughtful about the materials they choose, and it brings an extra mathematical element to the challenge. Some challenges include suggested costs and budgets, and others will need to be established.

## Pricing Ideas

- Price all of the materials available, and give students a total budget.

- Materials that are in short supply or that are of easier use in solving the challenge can have higher prices.

- It doesn't matter what the prices are, but students really love high prices—they love to pretend that they're spending millions!

- Connect the prices to your math lessons. Use prices that will force them to add with decimals or to multiply by 10.

You can fill in a *Price Sheet* (See page 9.) and give students *Budget Sheets* (See page 10.) to help them keep track of their spending. Always remind them that their budget must cover their original plan as well as any improvements they make, so students need to keep some money in reserve at first.

Here is an example price list for the *Green Roofs* challenge using small amounts of money. The amounts are specifically chosen to be easy to add and multiply.

| The budget is $5.00 | |
|---|---|
| **Item** | **Price** |
| potting soil | 10 cents per cup |
| pebbles | 5 cents per cup |
| marbles | 5 cents per cup |
| pipe cleaners | 5 cents each |
| cardboard | 10 cents per piece |
| newspaper | 10 cents per page |
| plastic bags | 25 cents each |
| foil | 25 cents per sheet |
| plastic wrap | 50 cents per sheet |
| cotton balls | 75 cents for 5 |
| sponges | $1 each |

Name _____    Date _____

# Price Sheet

The budget is _____.

Challenge:

| Item | Price |
|---|---|
|  |  |
|  |  |
|  |  |
|  |  |
|  |  |
|  |  |
|  |  |
|  |  |
|  |  |
|  |  |
|  |  |
|  |  |
|  |  |

| Total Spending: | |
|---|---|

Name _____     Date _____

# Budget Sheet

## Directions

1. List the name of your challenge at the top of the chart.
2. List each item that you will be using and its price.
3. Total your spending in the box below.

| Total budget for this challenge: |
| --- |
| _____ |

**Challenge:**

| Original Plan | | | |
| --- | --- | --- | --- |
| Item | Price | How Many? | Total |
|  |  | x |  |
|  |  | x |  |
|  |  | x |  |
|  |  | x |  |
|  |  | x |  |
|  |  | How much did we spend? |  |

Budget: _____

Spent: −_____

Left to spend: _____

| Improved Plan | | | |
| --- | --- | --- | --- |
| Item | Price | How Many? | Total |
|  |  | x |  |
|  |  | x |  |
|  |  | x |  |
|  |  | x |  |
|  |  | x |  |
|  |  | How much did we spend? |  |

Amount spent on original plan: _____

Amount spent on improved plans: +_____

Total amount spent: _____

| Did you complete the challenge within the budget? |
| --- |
| Yes    No |

# Challenge Overview

Each challenge in the series follows a similar layout to enable both teacher and students to have a clear picture of what is needed, what is expected, and how outcomes will be presented at the end of the challenges. Each challenge is introduced with a page providing the following information:

## Objectives

States specifically what students will do in each of the challenges.

## STEM Focus

Lists the main science concepts, science and engineering focus, science and engineering practices, and crosscutting concepts. (See page 112 for a chart of Performance Expectations, DCIs, SEPs, and CCCs.)

## Setup

Details teacher preparation for each activity, including materials to be gathered, copied, or prepared in advance.

## Materials

Lists materials needed for each Mini and Main Challenge—these are often flexible, so materials you have on hand may be substituted.

**Teacher Note:** It is assumed that students will have paper, pencils, crayons or markers, and scissors available for each challenge.

## Time Frame

Delineates approximate time for each phase of the challenge. Most challenges can be completed in one or two class meetings. Challenges may take longer when observations over time are required.

Make certain that students have adequate time to complete their Writing Reflections.

## Vocabulary

These vocabulary words are specific to the challenge and should be used both in discussions and in write-ups.

# Challenge Overview

Subsequent pages in the challenge are presented in this order:

## Introduction

Offers a guided, teacher-led introduction and lead-in to the Mini Challenge. The Introduction provides physical and verbal prompts, cues to make connections, and questions to guide explorations.

## The Mini Challenge

Provides scaffolding concepts and hands-on experience to prepare students for the Main Challenge.

Where appropriate, additional information is provided for students in the form of short reading passages and recording sheets, charts, and mini-posters.

## The Main Challenge

Presents a challenge designed for students to experience either the engineering design process or scientific inquiry.

Where appropriate, additional information is provided for students in the form of short reading passages and recording sheets, charts, and mini-posters.

## Analyze & Evaluate

Provides prompts and discussion questions to help analyze data, compare conclusions and solutions, and help students internalize concepts. This debriefing time is crucial to each challenge and should not be excluded.

## Reflections

Writing-reflection prompts are provided at the end of each challenge for students to restate their actions and learning, delineate learned concepts, and process their individual experiences. These can be compiled into individual science journals if desired.

## Extensions

When appropriate, ideas are provided to extend explorations, consider other approaches, and apply new knowledge in various situations.

# STEM Vocabulary for Every Challenge

The following vocabulary words are used in STEM. Discuss these terms as they come up and use them often during the different challenges.

**analyze**—to think about; to examine in detail; to make connections

**brainstorm**—generate a number of ideas very quickly without analyzing them

**build**—to create or make

**communicate**—to share information with others either verbally or in writing

**constraints**—rules, limitations, or restrictions that engineers or designers must work within

**data**—facts, information, and observations collected to be analyzed

**debrief**—a time to share data and observations and analyze outcomes; a wrap-up

**design**—a drawing or a plan to show the look and function of something

**evaluate**—to make a judgment

**evidence**—objective, unbiased proof; facts

**experiment**—a test under controlled conditions

**hypothesis**—a prediction that can be tested

**invent**—to design an original solution, a modification, or an improvement

**model**—a simplified representation of a system used in order to explain and help make predictions

**modify**—to change or adjust

**observe**—to receive knowledge of the outside world through our senses, or to record information using scientific tools and instruments

**plan**—a detailed proposal, drawing, or diagram

**record**—to write down information or data for later reference

**solution**—a means of solving a problem

**variable**—something that can change or be changed

# Engineering Design Process

—a series of steps used by engineers to solve a problem—

## Define the Problem
- What is the problem?
- Define the constraints.

## Imagine
- How can you approach the problem?
- Discuss ideas and possible solutions.
- Use your imagination.

## Plan
- Sketch your idea to solve the problem.
- List materials and steps to create your solution.

## Create
- Follow your plan.
- Build your solution.

## Test
- Try it out!
- Record results.

## Analyze & Evaluate
- Evaluate your results.
- What works or needs changes?

## Improve
- Make it better.

## Share & Reflect
- Share your results—what did you learn?
- Compare your solution to others.
- What would you like to try next?

*TCR 8185 STEM*

# Scientific Inquiry

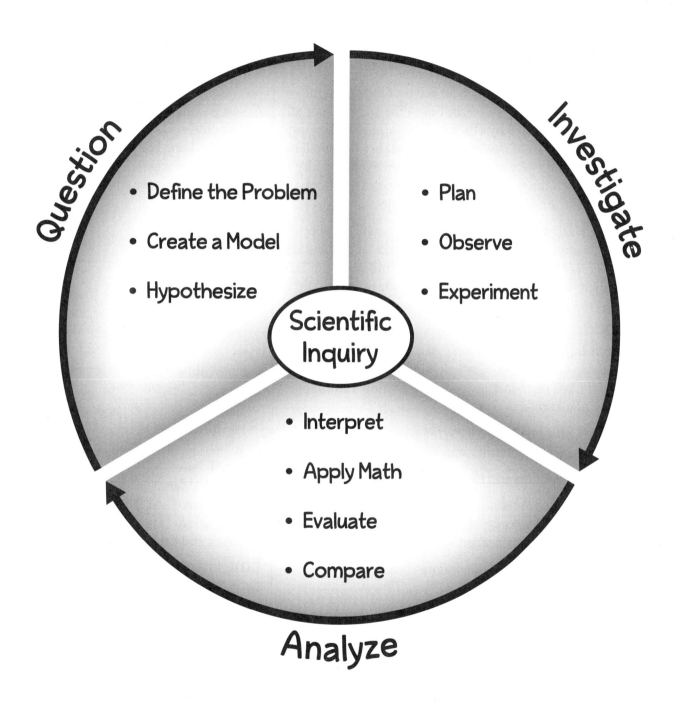

Question

Investigate

Analyze

- Define the Problem
- Create a Model
- Hypothesize

Scientific Inquiry

- Plan
- Observe
- Experiment

- Interpret
- Apply Math
- Evaluate
- Compare

# Fun with Bernoulli

## Objectives

Students will learn about air pressure and the Bernoulli principle through a series of hands-on activities. They will then design and create a toy using what they have learned.

## STEM Focus

*Physical Science:* Matter of any type can be subdivided into particles that are too small to see, but even then, the matter still exists and can be detected by other means. A model showing that gases are made from matter particles that are too small to see and are moving freely around in space can explain many observations, including the inflation and shape of a balloon and the effects of air on larger particles or objects.

*Engineering Design:* Define a simple design problem reflecting a need or a want that includes specified criteria for success and constraints on materials, time, or cost. Plan and carry out fair tests in which variables are controlled and failure points are considered to identify aspects of a model or a prototype that can be improved.

*Science and Engineering Practices:* Ask questions and define problems; plan and carry out investigations; analyze and interpret data; use mathematics and computational thinking; construct explanations.

*Crosscutting Concepts:* Cause and effect; energy and matter; scale, proportion, and quantity; stability and change

## Setup For Introduction and Mini Challenge

▶ Make copies of *Bernoulli's Principle Activity Cards, All About Bernoulli's Principle,* and *Bernoulli's Principle— Station by Station* as needed.

▶ Practice the demonstration before classes. (See page 17.)

▶ Each student should bring a copy of the activity page and a drinking straw to each station to avoid sharing germs.

▶ Set up two or three stations for each of the four activities (see *Bernoulli's Principle Activities*). Divide students into the same number of groups as you have stations.

## Setup For Main Challenge

▶ Make copies of *Bernoulli Toy Design* for each group.

▶ Provide tools such as scissors, glue, and staplers.

▶ Gather building materials you have on hand for this challenge.

## Materials

### Introduction and Mini Challenge

- *All About Bernoulli's Principle* (page 23)
- *Bernoulli's Principle—Station by Station* (pages 24–25)
- *Bernoulli's Principle Activity Cards* (pages 21–22)
- a fan that tilts upward
- balloons
- Ping-Pong balls
- sheets of paper
- straws (one per student)
- string
- thick books
- water-bottle funnels (page 19)
- yardsticks

### Main Challenge

- *Bernoulli Toy Design* (page 26)
- *Reflections—Fun with Bernoulli* (page 27)
- tape
- building materials (See Setup.)

### Suggestions

- * balloons
- * cardboard tubes
- * small battery-operated fans
- * soda cans
- * hair dryers
- * paper and cardstock
- * paper or plastic cups
- * plastic bottles
- * Ping-Pong balls
- * straws
- * string
- * tilting fans

## Time Frame

The Introduction and Mini Challenge takes about 45 minutes.

The first part of the Main Challenge will take about 40 minutes. The second part of the investigation should take about 45 minutes.

Follow up with the Writing Reflection as time allows.

## Vocabulary

air pressure
Bernoulli's principle
hover
molecule
theory

# Fun with Bernoulli

## Be Prepared!

1. Find a fan that tilts upward.

2. Blow up three or four balloons and tie them off.

3. Do a test run of the balloon demonstration prior to presenting it to the class. Place the balloon(s) into the column of air coming from the fan. The balloons should stay up, hovering and bumping around a bit in the column of air.

   → If the balloons are different sizes, they may move past each other and switch positions until the smallest balloon is on the bottom.

   → If the balloons don't stay in the air, create a tighter column of air by taping heavy cardstock or poster board into a tube with the diameter of the fan. Tape the column to the front of the fan. This should focus the air enough for the demonstration to work.

   → If you don't have a fan, you can do the same demonstration with a hair dryer set on cool and a Ping-Pong ball.

## Introduction

1. Point the fan straight up, and turn it on. Ask students:

   —What do you predict will happen when you place a balloon above the blowing fan?

2. Place a balloon into the stream of air.

3. Ask students to talk with a partner and to discuss what they just observed.

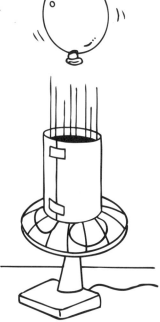

4. Then, ask students to share their explanations. Accept all explanations without comment at this time.

5. Add a second balloon, and discuss what happens.

6. Tell students that they just witnessed **Bernoulli's principle** in action.

 Write *Bernoulli's principle* on the board. Add student observations as the unit progresses.

7. Explain that Daniel Bernoulli was a mathematician and physicist who lived in Switzerland over 300 years ago! Let students know that in these challenges, they will have some fun learning how Bernoulli's principle works, and then build a toy or a game using this principle.

# Fun with Bernoulli

## Mini Challenge

### Teacher Preparation

Each station should include the following:

**Activity 1:** a piece of paper for each student

**Activity 2:** one piece of paper, two thick books

**Activity 3:** a yardstick, some string, and two blown-up balloons.

**Preparation:** Tie a string to each balloon, and tie the other ends to the yardstick. Slide the strings along the yardstick until the balloons are about 6 inches apart.

**Activity 4:** a Ping-Pong ball, a premade "water bottle" funnel for each student

**Preparation:** Water-bottle funnels are easy to make—simply cut the tops of the bottles off as shown and recycle the bottoms. If the cut edges are sharp, you can wrap them in duct or masking tape.

## Station Activities

1. Distribute a copy of *Bernoulli's Principle Activity Cards* to each group, along with a straw for each student. Remind students—no sharing straws!

2. Point out where each station is located. Have each group move to a station, complete the activity as directed on their recording sheets, and then move to a different station.

   Let students know that there are four different activities that need to be completed, but they can complete them in any order. If another group is busy at a station that they want to access, they should go to a free station that they haven't completed yet or wait patiently until the other group is finished.

3. Once students have competed all four activities, gather the students together and have each group share their results for each activity.

4. Discuss students' **theories** (*possible explanations*) about Bernoulli's principle and how it works.

5. Display or distribute *All About Bernoulli's Principle* and *Bernoulli's Principle—Station by Station* and review them both with students.

## Remember the fan and the balloons?

Demonstrate how Bernoulli's principle worked by having students act it out.

1. Have two students stand next to each other at one end of the room.

2. Give one student a straight path to the other end of the room, and give the second student a path that goes around several desks before getting to the other end.

3. Tell the students that they need to arrive at the other end of the room at the same time.

4. Have both students start walking at the same time. (*Notice that the student with the longer path must move faster to keep up with the student with the straight path. In the same way, the air moving around the balloon must move faster than the air farther away that is going straight.*)

# Fun with Bernoulli

## Main Challenge

### Define the Problem

1. Tell students that their challenge is to design and create a toy or a game using Bernoulli's principle. Their design should use fast-moving air to create an area of low pressure to make something move, bend, or **hover** (*remain in one place in the air*). Their game or toy can be very simple, but it must use Bernoulli's principle in some way.

2. Give each group a copy of *Bernoulli Toy Design*.

3. Review the Challenge Constraints and the Criteria for Success below. If appropriate, add budget information. (See pages 8–10.)

### Challenge Constraints

⚙ Use the Bernoulli principle in the operation of your toy or game.

⚙ Use only the materials given. You do not have to use all of the materials.

⚙ Your toy or game must be playable by anywhere from 1 to 3 people.

   If you will be challenging students by pricing objects and giving them a budget, add that to the list of constraints.

⚙ **Criteria for Success:** To be successful, your toy or game must use Bernoulli's principle to create a difference between high and low air pressure to make something move, bend, or hover.

4. Review the *Engineering Design Process* (page 14) with students. Remind them that they can test, improve, and retest more than once to get their toy or game working the way they want.

### Imagine and Plan

1. Show students the available materials, and give them time in their groups to brainstorm. Allow students to handle the materials while brainstorming. Remind them that, when brainstorming, every idea should be accepted, no matter how outlandish or impossible it sounds. You never know what might work or what might spark another idea.

2. After brainstorming, groups should work together to decide on which idea or ideas they will use in their toy plan.

3. Advise students that they may use tape in this challenge.

✏ Have students sketch their ideas, label their diagrams, and answer the questions on their *Bernoulli Toy Design* recording sheets.

# Fun with Bernoulli

## Main Challenge (cont.)

### Build and Test

1. Have students gather the materials, tape, and tools needed to build their toy according to their plans.

2. Circulate among the groups to observe and ask questions for formative evaluation, such as:

   —How will this toy use the Bernoulli principle?

   —How will low pressure be created?

   —What will move, bend, or hover?

3. Remind students that they need to explain how to play with their toy or game.

✏ Have students write their instructions for playing the game on a separate sheet of paper. They can be added to their *Bernoulli Toy Design* recording sheet.

### Evaluate & Analyze

1. Have each group present their Bernoulli principle toy or game to the class. They should share the instructions and then demonstrate how the toy works.

2. Invite students in the audience to explain how the Bernoulli principle is at work in each group's toy. Ask:

   —Where is air moving fast to create low pressure?

   —What is moving, bending, or hovering?

3. Discuss the results as a class, and determine how successful each toy or game was in using the Bernoulli principle. Encourage students to cite evidence in their answers, such as, "In this toy, when you blow through the straw, the fast moving air goes around the Ping-Pong ball, which creates low pressure. The higher pressure outside keeps the ball floating."

### Writing Reflection

✏ Have students complete the *Reflections—Fun with Bernoulli* writing reflection individually.

### Extension

✏ Give students sheets of paper and challenge them to create paper airplanes that demonstrate the Bernoulli principle. Have a contest to see which plane flies the longest, farthest, or highest.

Name _____     Date _____

## Bernoulli's Principle Activity Cards

### Activity 1–Paper Flag

**Material**

- 1 piece of paper for each student

**Procedure**

1. Roll the paper into a tube, and then unroll it.
2. Hold the paper just below your mouth so that it curves down.
3. Predict what the paper will do when you blow down on it.

_____

_____

4. Blow!
   ➜ What happened?

_____

_____

### Activity 2–Paper Bridge

**Materials**

- 1 piece of paper
- 2 books

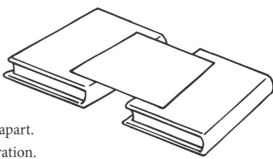

**Procedure**

1. Set the two books on the table about 6 inches apart.
2. Lay the paper across the books as in the illustration.
3. Predict what will happen when you use the straw to blow under the paper.

_____

4. Use your straw to blow between the books under the paper.
   ➜ What happened?

_____

5. Make sure that each student in your group takes a turn.

Name _____     Date _____

## Bernoulli's Principle Activity Cards *(cont.)*

### Activity 3–Friendly Balloons

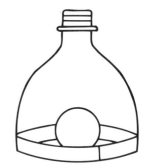

**Materials**

- two balloons
- yardstick
- string
- straws (one per student)

**Procedure**

1. Two students hold the yardstick as shown so that the balloons hang freely.

2. Predict what will happen when you blow between the balloons.

   _____

3. Use your straw to blow air between the balloons.

   ➜ What happens? _____

   _____

4. Take turns holding the yardstick so that each student gets a turn to blow.

### Activity 4–Keep the Ball in the Funnel

**Materials**

- water-bottle funnels
- Ping-Pong balls

**Procedure**

1. Each student should use his or her own water-bottle funnel.

2. Place the Ping-Pong ball on the table and place the water-bottle funnel upside down over it.

3. Predict what will happen when you blow through the funnel.

   _____

4. Blow!

   ➜ What happens?

   _____

# All About Bernoulli's Principle

**Air pressure** is pushing on us all the time. Air **molecules** exert a certain amount of pressure, or push, on everything on Earth. In order to understand what's going on, you will need to visualize the air and its movement.

First, imagine that you can see the air all around you, pushing on everything, including your body.

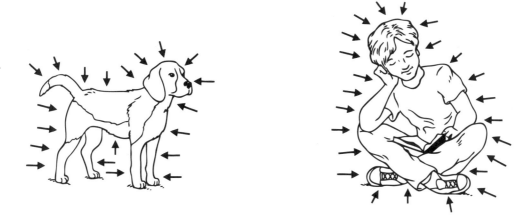

Then, pretend to blow out birthday candles, and visualize air moving away from your mouth as you blow. The air you blow moves faster than the air around it.

Bernoulli's principle states that the faster a fluid (in this case *air*) moves, the lower the pressure it puts on surrounding objects.

→ Slower moving or still air = more pressure
→ Faster moving air = less pressure

*Note:* Any substance that flows is considered a fluid—so yes *air* is a fluid!

# Bernoulli's Principle—Station by Station

Here is an explanation of how the Bernoulli principle works in each of the activities (stations).

## Activity 1–Paper Flag

When you blow across the top of the paper, you make the air move faster.

This means it exerts less pressure than the still air below the paper.

The higher pressure below the paper pushes the paper up toward the area of low pressure.

This is how airplanes fly—there is lower pressure as the air moves faster above the wings and higher pressure below (under the wings) as the air moves slower, which causes the wings to lift up.

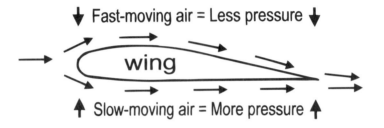

↓ Fast-moving air = Less pressure ↓

wing

↑ Slow-moving air = More pressure ↑

## Activity 2–Paper Bridge

When the air is still, the pressure above and below the paper is even, so the paper doesn't move.

As you blow under the paper, the faster-moving air underneath the paper has lower pressure than the still air above.

The higher pressure of the still air above the paper pushes it down toward the area of low pressure.

Slow-moving air = More pressure

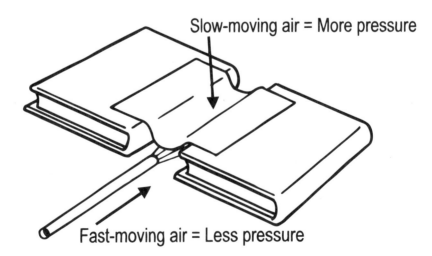

Fast-moving air = Less pressure

# Bernoulli's Principle—Station by Station

## Activity 3–Friendly Balloons

Blowing between the balloons causes the air between them to move faster, lowering the pressure. The higher pressure surrounding the balloons pushes them toward the area of low pressure.

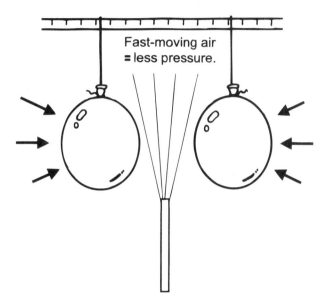

Fast-moving air = less pressure.

## Activity 4–Keep the Ball in the Funnel

As you blow down through the funnel, making the air move faster, the pressure in the funnel drops. The higher pressure of the surrounding air pushes the ball up into the funnel toward the area of low pressure.

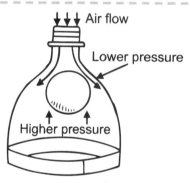

Air flow

Lower pressure

Higher pressure

Now, let's return to the balloons and the fan. When the air from the fan is moving past the balloon, the air closest to the balloon has to travel faster because it has to go farther to get around the balloon. The air farther away from the balloon just goes straight. This means that the fast-moving air closest to the balloon exerts less pressure than the slower-moving air farther away from the balloon. This keeps the balloon suspended in a "bubble" or a "pocket" of low pressure surrounded by higher pressure.

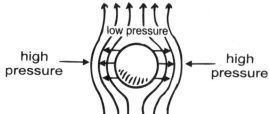

low pressure

high pressure          high pressure

Name _____    Date _____

# Bernoulli Toy Design

## Challenge Constraints

✪ Use Bernoulli's principle in the operation of your toy or game.

✪ Use only the materials given. You do not have to use all of the materials.

✪ Your toy or game must be playable by one to three people.

✪ **Criteria for Success:** To be successful, your toy or game must use Bernoulli's principle to create a difference between high and low air pressure to make something move, bend, or hover.

## Procedure

1. Look through the available materials, and brainstorm ideas for ways to make something move, bend, or hover using Bernoulli's principle.

2. Decide on how you will use the materials, and sketch your plan here. Label your diagram.

3. Explain how Bernoulli's principle works in your toy.

_____

_____

4. Test your toy. Did it work as planned?    **Yes    No**

   If not, explain what you think needs to be improved and how you will improve it.

_____

5. Continue testing and improving until your toy works as planned, or, if necessary, revise your plan. Describe what you did.

_____

6. Attach your instructions for playing with your toy or game to this page.

# Reflections—Fun with Bernoulli

1. Explain how your toy utilized Bernoulli's principle.

   _____

   _____

2. Draw and label a diagram showing how the air moves to create areas of lower and higher pressure.

   [ ]

3. Did you improve your design?    **Yes    No**

   How?

   _____

   _____

4. What did you learn from this challenge?

   _____

   _____

5. What was the hardest part?

   _____

   _____

6. What was your favorite part?

   _____

   _____

# Seed Growth Investigation

## Objectives

This challenge introduces students to variables and scientific investigation. Students will read a scenario in order to learn about variables in experiments. Then, students will design and carry out a scientific investigation to test their hypothesis about what seeds need to grow.

## STEM Focus

**Life Science:** Plants acquire their material for growth chiefly from air and water.

**Science Inquiry:** Support an argument that plants get the materials they need for growth chiefly from air and water.

**Science and Engineering Practices:** Ask questions; plan and carry out investigations; analyze and interpret data; use mathematics and computational thinking; construct explanations.

**Crosscutting Concepts:** Energy and matter

## Setup

### For Introduction and Mini Challenge

▶ Have a selection of the seeds listed for the Main Challenge ready to view.

### For Main Challenge

▶ You will need a dozen seeds that sprout quickly for each group.

--- Suggestions ---

| | | |
|---|---|---|
| * bean | * radish | * zinnia |
| * marigold | * sunflower | |
| * pea | * wheat grass | |

▶ Gather different types of containers for planting. Clear containers work best, but students may decide to test different types of containers, so provide additional options. Each group will need two or more identical containers, so gather multiples of each type.

--- Suggestions ---

| | |
|---|---|
| * cups | * milk cartons |
| * jars | * plastic bags |

▶ Arrange a space for some students' plants to receive sunlight, such as a windowsill, and for some to remain in the dark, perhaps in a closet.

## Materials

### Mini Challenge

- *Dr. X's Seed Test* (page 34)

### Main Challenge

- *Seed Test* (pages 35–36)
- *Reflections—Seed Growth Investigation* (page 37)
- containers for planting (See Setup.)
- rulers or tape measures
- seeds (See Setup.)
- soil
- water

## Time Frame

The Introduction and Mini Challenge will take about 40 minutes.

The Main Challenge should take about 50 minutes. Students should observe and record plant growth periodically over two weeks.

Follow up with the Writing Reflection as time allows.

## Vocabulary

conclusion

experiment

hypothesis

predict

replicate

results

variable

— independent variable

— controlled variable

— dependent variable

# Seed Growth Investigation

## Introduction

1. Show students the seeds for this challenge. Ask:

   —What things do seeds need in order to grow?

2. Ask student pairs to brainstorm things that seeds need in order to grow.

✏ Have students write down their ideas. Later, they will add questions to their lists.

3. Have students share their lists with the class, and record student responses on the board or chart paper.

## Mini Challenge

### Part 1

1. Tell students that they are going to plan and conduct an **experiment** about what seeds need to grow.

2. Have each pair of students work with another pair to form groups of four. Ask each group to brainstorm questions about what seeds need to grow. For example:

   —Do seeds need soil to grow?

   —Will seeds watered with orange juice grow?

✏ Ask each group to collaborate and write their questions down to share later.

3. Provide time for each group to read its list of questions aloud. Let the groups know that, if they hear a question they did not think of, they are welcome to add it to their own lists.

4. Tell students that each group is going to design and carry out a test to answer one question about what seeds need to grow. To help do this, they are going to read a scenario, *Dr. X's Seed Test*.

5. Distribute or display *Dr. X's Seed Test*. Read the scenario all the way through together.

✏ Have each group work together to fill in the chart and to answer the questions. Review the definition of a variable. A **variable** is something that can be changed.

   Here are three different types of variables:

   ➜ **Independent variables** are variables that scientists *change* during an experiment. There should only be one independent variable in an experiment.

   ➜ **Controlled variables** are things that scientists *keep the same*, or don't change.

   ➜ **Dependent variables** are the things that scientists *measure* to see if there has been a change.

6. Project the *Variables* chart or re-create it on chart paper. Have groups share their answers and record them on the class chart. If groups disagree, ask them to cite their evidence and discuss until students understand each item. Here are the answers:

| Variables | Sample A | Sample B |
|---|---|---|
| Air | No | Yes |
| Water | Yes | Yes |
| Sunlight | Yes | No |
| Soil | Yes | Yes |

©*Teacher Created Resources*

# Seed Growth Investigation

## Mini Challenge *(cont.)*

### Part 2

1. Discuss students' answers to the final question on the student page. Lead students to see that because Dr. X changed two variables (*air and sunlight*), she can't be sure which one made the difference in seed growth—it could have been either. Ask:

   —How could Dr. X have performed her test to answer her question?

2. Have groups work together to write out procedures for a test that would answer the question.

3. Allow groups to share their test procedures and have the class discuss whether each test would be valid.

**In a test, only one variable should be changed, and all the others should remain the same.** (*If she wanted to test for the effects of air, she should have put both the cup and the bag in the sunlight or in the closet. If she wanted to test for the effects of sunlight, she should put both samples in the same type of container and put one in sunlight and one in the closet.*)

4. Go over the explanation of variables at the bottom of the *Dr. X's Seed Test* page. Ask students:

   —What should Dr. X's independent variable have been? (*air*)

   —What should her controlled variables have been? (*Everything else: soil, water, light*)

   —What would her dependent variable be? (*the height of the plants*)

   —How could she measure her dependent variable? (*with a ruler or a measuring tape*)

# Seed Growth Investigation

## Main Challenge

### Define the Problem

1. Revisit the class list of what seeds need in order to grow. Be sure that at least these four items are listed: *air, water, sun,* and *soil.*

2. Tell students that, for the upcoming experiment, they will ask questions about what seeds need in order to grow and then plan and conduct their own seed growth experiments.

### Plan

1. Place students in small groups. Give each group a copy of *Seed Test* and review it together. Ask students:

   —Why do you think it is necessary to write out everything about your planned tests?

2. Lead students to understand that, when scientists do an investigation, they want other scientists to be able to **replicate** it (*do the experiment in exactly the same way*) to see if they get the same **results** (*evidence; outcome*).

3. For the question to test, tell students that their group should go through the list of questions that they brainstormed earlier and that they choose one to test. The question should involve just one independent variable.

## Examples

   —Does a seed need sunlight to sprout? (*Independent variable = sunlight*)

   —Will seeds grow when watered with liquids other than water? (*Independent variable = liquid*)

4. Ask: "What is a **hypothesis**?" Lead students to understand that their hypothesis should be the answer to their question—an answer that they think, or **predict**, will result from their test.

## Examples

| Question | Hypothesis |
|---|---|
| Do plants need soil in order to grow? <br> Will seeds grow when watered with soda instead of water? | Plants need soil to grow. <br> Seeds will grow when watered with soda. |

# Seed Growth Investigation

## Main Challenge *(cont.)*

### Plan *(cont.)*

5. Remind students to list each variable on their chart. At a minimum, they should list *air*, *water*, *sunlight*, *soil*, and *the container* in which they will grow their seeds.

**Only one variable, the independent variable, should be changed, and the rest, the controlled variables, should be the same.**

✍ Have students fill in the *Variable Chart* with *Yes* or *No* in each space and record their independent variable.

6. Ask students:

—What will you measure to find out if your independent variable affected your seeds' growth? Explain to students that what they observe and measure is the dependent variable. (In most cases, their dependent variable will be the height of the plant, which they will measure with a ruler or a tape measure.)

7. Allow groups to look over the available materials and to select what they need for their test. They should list their materials on their recording page.

8. Explain to students that the *Procedure* should consist of numbered steps telling how to complete their investigation. They should include everything they plan to do and not leave anything out. They may want to record their steps on a separate paper if they need more room.

9. Hold a meeting with each group to review their plan and help them make any corrections or adjustments. Once all groups have been approved, give them access to the materials and time to set up their tests.

10. As a class, talk about how students will record their results. Ask:

—How often will you measure and record your data?

# Seed Growth Investigation

## Main Challenge *(cont.)*

### Test

1. Over the next two weeks, set aside time for students to measure their samples and record their data according to their plans.

2 Once students have finished recording data, have a class meeting to analyze the results. Together, look at the blank graph. Ask:

—What values should go on the vertical scale? (*The measured heights of the plants.*)

—What values should go on the horizontal scale? (*The number of days.*)

3. Have students graph their data.

### Analyze & Evaluate

1. Have each group review its data and write its **conclusion**. Ask each group to answer these questions:

—What does the data show?

—Was your hypothesis proven either true or false?

—How does your data, or evidence, support your conclusion?

**It is not a problem if the group's conclusion proved its hypothesis wrong. Even if the hypothesis is supported by the data, more or different evidence could arise later that could disprove it. Scientists are not trying to be "right" in their hypotheses, they only want to find out what the evidence shows.**

2. Have each group present its test to the class. Group members should state their hypothesis, their variables, their procedure, their results, and their conclusion.

### Writing Reflection

✏ Have each student complete the *Reflections—Seed Growth Investigation* writing reflection individually.

### Extensions

- Let students run a second experiment to test a different hypothesis. Encourage them to do something interesting, such as test whether different colors of light or types of music affect seed or plant growth.

- Save any successfully sprouted plants to use in the *Break It Down* challenge (pages 38–47).

Name _____ Date _____

# Dr. X's Seed Test

## Scenario

Dr. X. Periment asks the question, "Is air necessary for seeds to grow?"

She places some soil in a bag and pushes three seeds into the soil. Then, she puts some water in and squeezes the air out of the bag. Dr. X then seals the bag so that there is little or no air for the seeds. She labels the bag **Sample A** and puts it in direct sunlight. Dr. X also puts a small amount of soil in a cup and presses three seeds into it. She leaves the cup uncovered so that the seeds in this sample have plenty of air. Dr. X sprinkles some water on the seeds and puts the cup in the closet. She labels this cup **Sample B**.

**Directions:** The variables that Dr. X used in her test are in the first column. For each sample (**A** and **B**), write *Yes* if the variable was present or *No* if it was not.

| Variables | Sample A | Sample B |
|---|---|---|
| Air | | |
| Soil | | |
| Water | | |
| Sunlight | | |

Dr. X waited a week and then observed her seeds again. Here is what she observed:

→ **Sample A**—The seeds in the bag had started to sprout.

→ **Sample B**—The seeds in the cup did not sprout.

Dr. X. Periment concluded that seeds don't need air to grow since there was no air in Sample A.

Do you think she is right?      **Yes      No**

Why or why not?

_____

_____

Name _____     Date _____

# Seed Test

**Directions:** Use the outline below to design your seed test.

1. The **question** we will try to answer is: _____

   _____

2. Our **hypothesis** is: _____

   _____

3. List the variables in the chart below and mark whether or not each is present in your seed test samples.

| Variables | Sample A | Sample B |
|-----------|----------|----------|
| Air       |          |          |
|           |          |          |
|           |          |          |
|           |          |          |

4. **Independent variable:** _____

5. **Dependent variable:** _____

   How will you measure your dependent variable? _____

   _____

6. **Materials:**

   _____  _____  _____  _____

   _____  _____  _____  _____

7. **Procedure:** _____

   _____

   _____

Name _____     Date _____

# Seed Test *(cont.)*

**Directions:** Record your data, graph your results, and write your conclusion.

8. **Data:** _____

_____

_____

_____

9. **Results:** _____

_____

_____

10. **Conclusion:** _____

_____

_____

Name _____  Date _____

# Reflections—Seed Growth Investigation

1. What was your question about seeds?

   _____

   _____

2. What was your hypothesis?

   _____

   _____

3. How did you test your hypothesis?

   _____

   _____

4. What were your results?

   _____

   _____

5. What did you learn from this experiment?

   _____

   _____

6. What was the hardest part?

   _____

   _____

7. What was your favorite part?

   _____

   _____

8. What plant experiment would you like to do next?

   _____

   _____

# Break It Down

## Objectives

Students will test different materials to find out if the materials will decay. Then, they will design and create biodegradable seedling planters.

## STEM Focus

*Life Science:* Some organisms, such as fungi and bacteria, break down dead organisms (*both plants or plants parts and animals*) and therefore operate as "decomposers." Decomposition eventually restores (*recycles*) some materials back to the soil.

*Engineering Design:* Define a simple design problem reflecting a need or a want that includes specified criteria for success and constraints on materials, time, or cost. Generate and compare multiple possible solutions to a problem based on how well each is likely to meet the criteria and constraints of the problem.

*Science and Engineering Practices:* Plan and carry out investigations; construct explanations and design solutions.

*Crosscutting Concepts:* Energy and matter; systems and system models

## Setup For Mini Challenge

▶ Have students save biodegradable and nonbiodegradable materials from their lunches or bring them from home. Collect trash or recyclable items: paper and cardboard, plastic and paper milk cartons, paper towels and napkins, food wrappers or containers, plastic wrap, aluminum foil or cans.

▶ Include some connecting materials such as staples, paper clips, string, rubber bands, and glue. These will also need to be tested.

## Setup For Main Challenge

▶ Once students have selected materials and designed their planters, they will need to gather enough of their chosen materials to build their planters.

▶ Students will need fast-sprouting seeds to plant in their planters. *Suggestions:* bean, marigold, pea, radish, sunflower, or zinnia

▶ Look for a garden space or a planter at school where students can plant their seedlings, or have students plant them in large, clear plastic bins filled with soil. If they plant one biodegradable planter close to the wall of the clear plastic bin, they can observe the roots growing and (hopefully) their planter decaying.

## Materials

### Introduction and Mini Challenge

- *What Decays?* (page 43)
- 1-gallon, clear plastic, resealable bags, one per group
- non-biodegradable and biodegradable materials (See Setup.)
- non-latex gloves
- soil
- straws
- trays, tarps, or plastic bins for sorting materials
- water
- wax paper or foil

### Main Challenge

- *Biodegradable Planters* (pages 44–45)
- *Reflections—Biodegradable Planters* (page 47)
- *How Long Does It Take?* (page 46) *optional*
- materials for building (See Setup for Mini Challenge.)
- seeds (See Setup.)
- potting soil
- water
- *optional:* clear, plastic bins

## Time Frame

The Introduction and Mini Challenge can be started in one class session of about 40 minutes, followed by a few minutes every other day for two weeks. After two weeks, you will need another 40-minute session for students to analyze the test results.

Allow at least an hour for the Main Challenge.

Follow up with the Writing Reflection.

## Vocabulary

| | |
|---|---|
| biodegradable | landfill |
| decay | seedling |
| decomposer | |

# Break It Down

## Introduction

1. Ask students if they have ever seen (or smelled!) food rotting. Have volunteers describe what they saw or smelled. Ask:

   —What happens to our trash after it is thrown it away? Where does it go?

2. Explain that there is no "away." Trash is taken to a **landfill** (*a designated location for trash*) where it is buried, or to a recycling center, where it can be recycled, and/or made into new products.

3. Explain to students that, in a landfill, if a material **decays**, it breaks down into smaller and smaller bits. This is how nature recycles materials—they are broken down and become part of the soil, which can then nourish plants. Ask:

   —What happens to materials in a landfill that do not decay? (*Explain that those materials remain the same, even over long periods of time. If they are in a landfill, they are buried. If they don't make it to a landfill, they become litter or pollution, and they can be harmful to the environment. You may wish to choose an example to share from "How Long Does It Take?" on page 46.*)

✍ Write **biodegradable** on the board or chart paper. Ask students to use the parts of the word to determine its meaning. (*Bio is a prefix meaning "life." Degrade means "to break down into smaller pieces."*)

4. So, if something is *biodegradable*, it means that living things, like bacteria, can break it down. Biodegradable materials decay and are recycled back into the environment.

5. Tell students that in this challenge, they will test materials to see if the materials are biodegradable and then use what they learn to design biodegradable seedling planters.

## Mini Challenge

### Part 1

1. Explain to students that they will be designing and making planters to grow **seedlings**. Seedlings are fragile, young plants, just sprouted from their seeds.

2. Students will create small pots or containers in which seeds can sprout, and then the container can be planted in the soil. These containers will protect the fragile, new plants and later biodegrade so that the plants can spread their growing roots into the soil.

3. As a class, brainstorm materials that students might use to build planters, such as paper, cardboard, plastic, glass, and metal. Make a list on the board or chart paper of specific examples, such as plastic or paper milk cartons, paper towels and napkins, writing or construction paper, food wrappers or containers, and aluminum foil or cans.

4. Over the next few days, gather these materials for the "Biodegradability Test" students will perform. Have them save leftover packaging and trash from their lunches, or bring items from home.

5. Students will also need to test any connecting materials they might want to use in building their planters, such as staples, paper clips, string, rubber bands, and glue. **Note:** If the connecting materials aren't biodegradable, they can't use them! They can test glue by setting out a small puddle on wax paper or foil and peeling it up after it is dry. They can cut off a small chunk of glue stick and test that as well.

# Break It Down

## Mini Challenge

### Part 2

1. Have students form working groups of three or four, and select five materials to test. Make sure each group tests some different materials so that as many materials as possible are being tested across the class. All groups will combine their data at the end of the Mini Challenge.

2. Have students cut a 1" square of each material, making them as uniform as possible. Don't forget to include the material used to hold the planters together. Have students sketch and label the squares on the *What Decays?* recording sheet.

3. If possible, have students photograph the materials as well.

**Be sure students include both biodegradable materials like cardboard and paper and non-biodegradable materials like plastic and aluminum foil so they can observe the difference between organic and inorganic materials in their results.**

4. Give each group a one-gallon resealable, clear plastic bag. Have students place the material samples in their bags.

5. Point out that living organisms are necessary to break these items down. Ask:

   —Where can we get some bacteria, fungi, and/or other living organisms (*decomposers*) to break down our biodegradable materials?

6. Explain to students that **decomposers** are usually present in living material and in soil. Add some plant material (*apple cores, fruit rinds, leftover vegetables, etc.*) to each bag, along with a couple of small scoops of soil.

7. Have students add a sprinkle of water—just enough to make everything in the bag damp. Have students close their bags almost all the way, leaving a small opening in which to insert a piece of a straw to let air circulate in and out of the bag. Explain that adding a bit of water and allowing oxygen in will help the decomposers and speed up the decay.

### Part 3

1. Set the bags in an undisturbed area that recieves sunlight. Have students add a small amount of water to each bag and have them knead the bags to mix the materials once every few days.

2. After two weeks, have students open their bags and dump the contents onto a tray or tarp, or into a plastic bin. Have them wear gloves as they sort through the materials and attempt to identify them.

   *Note:* If they photographed the materials earlier, have them compare what they see now to the way the materials looked before the test.

3. Have students examine each material sample and sketch and describe it on their *What Decays?* recording sheets. If they can't find a material, that means it has decayed, and they should document that fact.

4. Create a class T-chart with the headings *Biodegradable* and *Non-Biodegradable*. Have each group add their materials in the appropriate column to create a reference chart for the entire class.

# Break It Down

## Main Challenge

### Define the Problem

1. Tell students that, in the Main Challenge, they will design and make biodegradable seedling planters using their research results from the Mini Challenge.

2. Distribute a copy of *Biodegradable Planters* to each group. Read it together and answer questions.

3. Discuss the Challenge Constraints and the Criteria for Success with the class. Mention that they can find a copy of these constraints on their recording sheets. If appropriate, include budget information.

### Challenge Constraints

⚙ Use only biodegradable materials to make seedling planters.

⚙ You must be able to plant six seeds, each seed in a separate container or section, in your planter or planters.

⚙ The containers or sections can be connected or separate. If they are connected, there must be at least 6" between the seeds.

⚙ **Criteria for Success:** To be successful, planters must hold together for a few days when filled with moist soil to give the seeds a chance to sprout before they are planted.

### Imagine & Plan

1. Give students time to brainstorm ideas and make a plan for their seedling planters.

2. Remind students that their planters can only use biodegradable materials, which means that anything used to hold them together must also be biodegradable.

3. Review the *Engineering Design Process* (page 14) with students. Remind them that they can test, improve, and retest as much as they like in the time available. Let them know how much time they have.

### Build • Test • Improve

1. Have students gather the materials to build their planters.

2. Circulate, as students are working, in order to observe and ask questions for formative evaluation, such as:

   —What materials are you using?

   —Are you sure they're biodegradable? How do you know?

   —How will the planter hold together while the seeds sprout?

3. Give students potting soil and seeds, and have them plant the seeds in their planters. They will need to sprinkle a bit of water on them as well.

4. Set the planters in a sunny spot where they won't be disturbed. Have students lightly water their seeds every other day.

# Break It Down

## Main Challenge *(cont.)*

### Build • Test • Improve (cont.)

5. After five to seven days (*depending on the type of seeds used*), have students check their seedlings and their planters.

✎ They should record their observations on their *Biodegradable Planters* recording sheets.

6. If their planters are falling apart, allow them time and materials to make improvements. They should be able to very gently remove the failing container and place the soil with the seedling in an improved version.

### Analyze & Evaluate

1. Bring the class together, and have each group give a short presentation about how they designed and built their planter. Ask them to share the following information:

   → Which biodegradable materials were used?

   → How did you come to your design decisions?

   → What, if any, improvements were made?

2. Bring the class together to debrief. Talk about each planter design's strengths and weaknesses. Have students share ideas for improvements.

3. Have students plant their seedlings in a garden or in large, clear plastic bins filled with soil.

**If they plant one biodegradable planter close to the wall of the plastic bin, they may be able to observe the roots growing and their planter decaying.**

4. Have each group make plant markers to identify their plants. If you have a school garden or space in a planter on campus, have students replant their planters and label them. Remind students to water their plants regularly.

5. After a couple of weeks, have students inspect their plants and see if they are growing successfully.

6. Choose one "sacrificial" seedling to uproot to see if the biodegradable planter is decaying and to observe the plant's roots.

### Writing Reflection

✎ Have each student complete the *Reflections—Biodegradable Planters* writing reflection individually.

### Extension

Discuss the *How Long Does It Take?* survey with the class. As a class, create a chart showing the items in order from the one that takes the shortest amount of time to decompose to the item(s) that take the longest. Evaluate your findings:

—What can you do to create less waste in the landfill?

Name _____     Date _____

# What Decays?

## Directions

1. Fill in the **Before** date to show when you began this activity.

2. In the first column, sketch your sample of each material and label it.

3. Fill in the **After** date in the second column. Sketch each material that you found in the soil and describe how it has changed. Notice if the edges of your squares are still straight, if there are any holes, or if there are other signs that they are falling apart?

4. In the final column, mark how much time elapsed between the *Before* date and the *After* date and mark each material listed as *biodegradable* or *non-biodegradable*.

| Before _____ | After _____ | Total Time _____ |
|---|---|---|
| | | ☐ biodegradable<br>☐ non-biodegradable |
| | | ☐ biodegradable<br>☐ non-biodegradable |
| | | ☐ biodegradable<br>☐ non-biodegradable |
| | | ☐ biodegradable<br>☐ non-biodegradable |
| | | ☐ biodegradable<br>☐ non-biodegradable |

Name _____     Date _____

# Biodegradable Planters

**Directions:** Create a seedling planter according to these constraints.

### Challenge Constraints

⚙ Make seedling planters using only biodegradable materials.

⚙ The planter or planters must be able to plant six seeds, each seed in a separate container or section.

⚙ The containers or sections can be connected or separate. If they are connected, there must be at least six inches between the seeds.

⚙ **Criteria for Success:** To be successful, the planters must hold together for a few days when filled with moist soil to give the seeds a chance to sprout before they are planted. They must break down when planted in soil, allowing the plants roots to spread.

## Procedure

1. Choose three biodegradable materials from the class chart to use for your planters.

2. Brainstorm two ideas for the planter and sketch them. You can combine materials if you want.

| Idea 1 | Idea 2 |
|---|---|
| | |

3. Select one idea to execute and circle it above in your sketch.

4. Create your seedling planter.

Name _____     Date _____

# Biodegradable Planters

## Procedure *(cont.)*

5. After your seedling has sprouted, draw your planter and seedling here.

```
[                                                              ]
```

6. Evaluate your planter.  Did it meet the criteria for success?      **Yes**      **No**

   Why or why not?

   _____

   _____

   _____

7. If your planter failed to hold the soil and seedling, analyze why you think it failed and think about how you could fix it or create a new, better planter.

   _____

   _____

   _____

8. Make your improvements, or create a new planter and very gently transfer your seedling into it.

Name _____     Date _____

# How Long Does It Take?

Here is a list of biodegradable and non-biodegradable items and approximately how long it takes each one to decompose.

## Directions

✔ Put a check mark next to each item you or someone in your family uses.

— Draw a line through the items your family does not use.

☺ Put a happy face next to the item on the list of items that you use that decomposes the fastest.

☹ Put a sad face next to the item on the list of items that your family uses that takes the longest to decompose.

| | | | |
|---|---|---|---|
| paper towel | 2–4 weeks | leather shoe | 25–40 years |
| banana peel | 3–4 weeks | nylon clothes | 30–40 years |
| newspaper | 2–6 weeks | styrofoam cup | 50 years |
| paper bag | 4 weeks | tin can | 50 years |
| apple core | 4–8 weeks | aluminum can | 200–500 years |
| paper (sheet) | 12 weeks | plastic water bottle | 450 years |
| cotton t-shirt | 4–20 weeks | plastic 6-pack ring | 450 years |
| orange peel | 6 months | diaper | 450+ years |
| balloon | 6 months | fishing line | 600 years |
| rope | 3–14 months | styrofoam tray | maybe never |
| wool sock | 1–5 years | plastic bags | 200–1000 years |
| milk carton | 5 years | plastic milk jug | maybe never |
| cigarette | 10–12 years | glass bottle | 1–2 million years |
| wooden baseball bat | 20 years | | |

Name _____ Date _____

# Reflections—Biodegradable Planters

1. Which material samples in your bag decayed?

_____

2. Which material samples in your bag did not decay?

_____

3. What materials did you use to build your planters?

_____     _____     _____

4. How did your group arrive at your final design?

_____

What decisions did you make?

_____

_____

5. What do you think went well?

_____

_____

6. What was your favorite part?

_____

_____

7. Which part was the hardest?

_____

_____

8. What surprised you?

_____

_____

# The Bubble Solution Investigation

## Objectives

Students will learn about surface tension through a series of hands-on activities. Students will then use the scientific process to find the best bubble-solution additive for making long-lasting bubbles.

## STEM Focus

*Life Science:* When two or more different substances are mixed, a new substance with different properties may be formed.

*Science Inquiry:* Conduct an investigation to determine whether the mixing of two or more substances results in new substances.

*Science and Engineering Practices:* Ask questions and define problems; plan and carry out investigations; analyze and interpret data; use mathematics and computational thinking; construct explanations.

*Crosscutting Concepts:* Cause and effect; energy and matter; scale, proportion, and quantity; stability and change

## Setup for Introduction and Mini Challenge

▶ Search "surface tension swimmer" online to find images that show swimmers as they stretch the surface of the water to create what looks like a glass bubble just before they break the surface tension.

▶ Set up two stations each for the three surface-tension activities, for a total of six stations. (See *Surface Tension Activity Cards* for materials needed.) Include copies of the Activity Cards at each station—one for each group (or student).

▶ Be sure that each student has his or her own straw so that students aren't sharing germs.

## Setup for Main Challenge

▶ Make the bubble solution ahead of time. Gently mix ⅔ cup of dish soap into one gallon of warm water. Distilled water works best, but tap water will do if it isn't too hard.

▶ Each group will need three cups, each labeled *Bubble Solution*. Pour one cup of basic bubble solution into each cup.

▶ For each group, premeasure additives into three smaller, labeled cups: one with 1 T. of glycerin, one with 1 T. of corn syrup, and one with 2 T. of sugar.

## Materials
### Introduction and Mini Challenge

- *Water Molecules* (page 54)
- *Surface Tension Activity Cards* (page 53)
- photo of swimmer (See Setup.)
- black pepper
- dish soap
- paper clips
- pennies
- plastic bowls, cups, and plates
- straws
- timer
- toothpicks
- water

### Main Challenge

- *Bubble Solutions Test* (pages 55–56)
- *Reflections—Bubble Solution Investigation* (page 57)
- dish soap
- glycerin
- light corn syrup
- paper towels
- plastic cups
- straws and pipe cleaners
- sugar
- water (distilled and tap)

## Time Frame

The Introduction and Mini Challenge should take about 45 minutes.

The first part of the Main Challenge will take about 40 minutes. The second part of the investigation should take about 45 minutes. Bubbles should be made the day before the activity.

Follow up with the Writing Reflection as time allows.

## Vocabulary

| | |
|---|---|
| additive | mean |
| cohesion | reproducibility |
| conclusion | surface |
| control | surface tension |

# The Bubble Solution Investigation

*Teacher Note*

This challenge is best presented after the Seed Growth challenge, which introduces students to variables and scientific investigation.

## Introduction

1. Show students a photo of a swimmer as he or she stretches the **surface** (*top or outer layer*) of the water to create what looks like a glass bubble. Ask students:

   —What do you think is going on in the picture of the swimmer? (*Allow time for discussion.*)

2. Tell students that they will do three quick, hands-on activities, each for five minutes, to learn about the phenomenon that they see in the photo.

## Mini Challenge

1. Divide students into six groups—one for each station. Have each group move to a station and perform the activity at that station.

2. After 5 minutes, signal students to move to another station with an activity they have not yet completed. After 5 more minutes, signal again and have students move to their last activity station.

3. Have each group share with the class their results for each activity. As a class, discuss students' theories about why water behaves the way that it does.

4. Share the *Water Molecules* information sheet with the class. Take time to discuss the meaning of surface tension and review the graphics. Ask:

   —Does this information change your theories about water behavior? If so, how?

5. Ask students to focus on the pepper and penny activities. Ask:

   —What do you think soap does to water molecules?

6. Give students a few minutes to discuss this question in their groups. Then, have one member each group share their ideas with the class. (*Students will probably agree that soap breaks or lessens the surface tension of the water.*)

✎ Provide time for students to add soap molecules to the information sheet.

## Explain the Science

The soap molecules get between the water molecules at the surface and increase the distance between the water molecules. This decreases the pull that the water molecules have on each other, lowering the surface tension of the solution.

Tell students that this will play a part in the next investigation.

# The Bubble Solution Investigation

## Main Challenge

### Part 1—Blowing Bubbles

1. Provide each group with a small cup of water, a straw for each student, and some paper towels.

2. Tell students to dip the end of their straw into the water, lift it up, and try to blow a bubble on the end. Ask:

   —Can you explain why the water won't form a bubble?
   (*The surface tension of the water is too strong—it can't stretch, so it breaks.*)

3. Ask students how they could reduce the surface tension of the water. That's right—soap!

4. Show students the bubble solution you prepared earlier (the day before, if possible) and explain that you have added soap to the water. Provide each group with a small amount of pre-mixed bubble solution (about ½ inch deep in a small cup) and have them try blowing bubbles by dipping the ends of their straws in the solution, lifting the straw up, and blowing through it. They will need to blow gently at first.

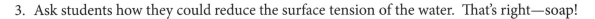

## Explain the Science

Each bubble is formed by inner and outer layers of soap, with the water layer in the middle. The soap reduces the surface tension of the water, allowing it to stretch. Bubbles will eventually pop when the water is stretched too far, or if the water evaporates. It will also pop if the bubble comes in contact with something dry that breaks the surface tension.

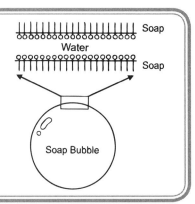

5. Tell students that, in this investigation, they will add different substances to the bubble solution to see which one makes the largest bubbles. Ask students,

   —How would you measure a bubble floating in the air? (*They should conclude that it would be very difficult!*)

6. Have students try to blow a bubble on the dry surface of the table by dipping a straw into the bubble solution and blowing a bubble right onto the table. (*The bubble should pop very quickly.*)

7. Next, have students wet the surface of the table—they can just wet their fingers with a little bit of water and rub it on the table. Have them try blowing a bubble on the wet table. They should be able to blow a fairly large bubble.

8. Once their bubble pops, ask if they can measure the size of the bubble. (*They should see an outline of the bubble on the table that they can measure with a ruler.*)

# The Bubble Solution Investigation

## Main Challenge *(cont.)*

### Part 2—Preparing for the Tests

1. Tell students that you will give them three different substances that may make it possible for them to blow bigger bubbles. Explain that each **additive** (*added substance*) works in the same way—it slows the evaporation of the water so that the bubbles will last longer, allowing time to make them bigger before they pop. Students will test each substance to find which additive works best.

✏ Write the word *additive* and its definition on the board.

2. Give each group three separate, labeled cups, each containing one cup of basic bubble solution.

3. Next, give each group three smaller, labeled cups containing the premeasured additives:

   → **Cup 1**—1 tablespoon of glycerin (available at drug stores)

   → **Cup 2**—1 tablespoon of corn syrup

   → **Cup 3**—2 tablespoons of sugar

4. Allow students to inspect the additives closely. They can touch each one with the tip of a finger and feel the textures. Remind students not to put any substances in their mouths.

5. Have students pour each additive into a different cup of bubble solution. Stir each mixture gently.

6. Give each group a copy of the *Bubble Solutions Test* recording sheets. Read through it together, and work with students to fill it in.

✏ Have students fill in the investigation specifics as shown below.

   **The question we will try to answer is:** Which bubble solution additive will make the biggest bubble?

   **Hypothesis** (*what we think will happen*): Have students write what they predict the outcome will be. For example, "We think the glycerin will make the biggest bubbles."

   **Independent variable** (*the thing we will change*): The additive to the solution will change.

   **Dependent variable** (*the thing we will measure*): The size of the bubbles will be measured.

   **We will measure our dependent variable by:** We will measure the outline of the bubble on the table. (*Decide as a class whether to measure in inches or centimeters.*)

   **Reminder:** Caution students to wipe away each outline after it has been measured and to slightly wet the table again to prepare for the next bubble.

   **Controlled variables** (*everything else*): Ask students what other variables they can think of.

   ### Examples

   - the strength of the blow
   - the straw
   - the surface the bubbles are blown on
   - the temperature of the solution

# The Bubble Solution Investigation

## Main Challenge (cont.)

7. Explain that to really know which additive made the difference, everything else about how they create the bubbles must be the same. Also, they will test plain soap and water as a **control** to which they can compare the different additives.

> **Materials:** Have students list all the materials they will use.

> **Procedure:** Have students write out a step-by-step procedure for the investigation. Remind them that the aim of the procedure is **reproducibility**—another scientist reading this should be able to replicate the test.

### Part 3–Testing Bubble Additives

1. Give students time to perform their tests and to record their data. Keep plenty of paper towels handy!

2. Students should calculate the **mean** (*average*) bubble size for each additive and graph their data using the blank bar graph on their recording sheet.

3. Students should write their **conclusions** based on the analysis of their data. Remind them to state whether the results proved their hypothesis correct or incorrect.

4. Have each group present their hypothesis, data, and conclusions to the class.

5. As a class, discuss the results. Try to determine how successful each additive was versus the control, and which additive created the biggest bubbles.

6. Encourage students to cite evidence in their answers, such as, "More groups found that the glycerin made the biggest bubbles, so glycerin worked best."

7. Just for fun, challenge students to test their best solution by blowing a bubble within a bubble. The secret is wetting the straw so that it will go inside a bubble without breaking it. See how many bubbles-within-bubbles they can make!

### Writing Reflection

✏ Have students complete the *Reflections—Bubble Solution Investigation* writing reflection individually.

### Extensions

- Have students test different dependent variables, such as the longest-lasting bubble or the greatest number of connected bubbles.

- Have students engineer and test different bubble wands from materials such as straws, pipe cleaners, and string. They can try to make lots of small bubbles, really huge bubbles, or bubbles stacked into different formations.

# Surface Tension Activity Cards

## Activity 1–Will it Float?

**Materials**

- 1 cup of water
- paper clip
- toothpick
- penny

1. Bend one end of a paper clip up slightly so that you can hold it.

2. Very gently lay the paper clip on the surface of the water.

   ➜ Can you get the paper clip to float?     **Yes     No**

3. Next, gently lay the toothpick on the surface of the water.

   ➜ Can you float the toothpick?     **Yes     No**

4. Finally, try to gently lay the penny on the surface of the water.

   ➜ Can you float the penny?     **Yes     No**

## Activity 2–Penny Dome

**Materials**

- 1 cup of water (labeled *plain water*)
- plate
- 1 cup of soapy water (labeled *soapy water*)
- straw
- pennies

1. Place a penny on the plate.

2. Dip one end of a straw about ¼ inch into the water, and place your thumb over the other end. This will keep a drop of water in the straw.

3. Next, keeping your thumb over the straw, move the straw so that the end with the water is just above the penny.

4. Release your thumb, and let the water drop onto the penny.

   ➜ How many drops can you add before the water runs off the penny? _____ drops

5. Dry the penny off, and repeat the activity with soapy water.

   ➜ How many drops could you add this time? _____ drops

## Activity 3–Pepper Party

**Materials**

- bowl of water
- pepper
- dish soap (1 tsp. in cup)

1. Shake pepper onto the surface of the water, just enough so that there is an even coating.

2. Touch your finger gently to the surface of the water in the center of the bowl.

   ➜ What happens? _____

3. Put a tiny bit of soap on your finger, and dip it into the center of the water again.

   ➜ What happens? _____

Name _____     Date _____

# Water Molecules

Water molecules attract each other and stick together—they love their neighbors.  This attraction is called **cohesion**.  The water molecules on the surface don't have as many "neighbor" water molecules to stick to, so they stick to each other with more strength.  This causes **surface tension**.

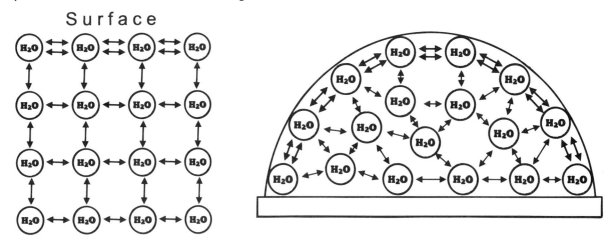

Surface tension forms a sort of skin on the water, which keeps the pepper and the paper clip from sinking, and forms a dome of water on the coin.  This is the same phenomenon that we saw in the photo of the swimmer.

**Directions**:  Add soap molecules in between the water molecules at the surface of the water molecule diagram.  The first one has been done for you.

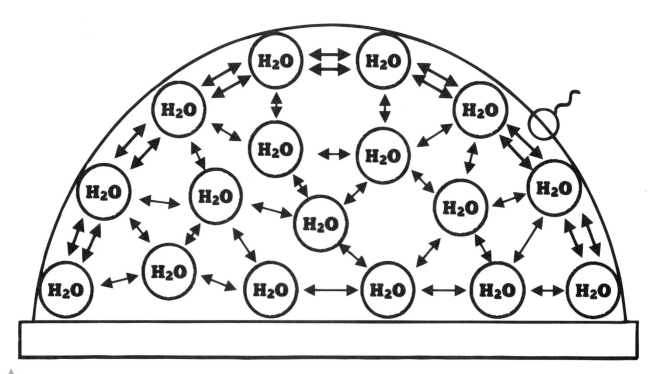

Name _____ Date _____

# Bubble Solutions Test

**Directions:** Use the scientific process to test bubble solution additives. Record your information below.

1. The **question** we will try to answer is: _____

_____

2. **Hypothesis** (*what we think will happen*): _____

_____

3. **Independent variable** (*the thing we will change*): _____

_____

4. **Dependent variable** (*the thing we will measure*): _____

_____

5. We will measure our **dependent variable** by: _____

_____

6. **Controlled variables** (*everything else*): _____

_____

_____

7. **Materials:**

_____  _____  _____

_____  _____  _____

_____  _____  _____

8. **Procedure:**

_____

_____

_____

Name _____    Date _____

# Bubble Solutions Test *(cont.)*

9. **Data:** Record your data in the table.  Test the control solution and each additive five times.

| Additive | Size of Bubble | Average Bubble Sizes | | | |
|---|---|---|---|---|---|
| Control: soap and water | 1. | | | | |
| | 2. | | | | |
| | 3. | | | | |
| | 4. | | | | |
| | 5. | | | | |
| Glycerin | 1. | | | | |
| | 2. | | | | |
| | 3. | | | | |
| | 4. | | | | |
| | 5. | | | | |
| Corn Syrup | 1. | | | | |
| | 2. | | | | |
| | 3. | | | | |
| | 4. | | | | |
| | 5. | | | | |
| Sugar | 1. | | | | |
| | 2. | | | | |
| | 3. | | | | |
| | 4. | | | | |
| | 5. | Control | Glycerin | Corn Syrup | Sugar |

10. Calculate the **mean** (*average*) bubble size for the control and for each additive.

➜ Control (*soap and water*): _____      ➜ Corn Syrup: _____

➜ Glycerin: _____      ➜ Sugar: _____

11. Graph your average bubble sizes on the graph on the right side above.

12. **Conclusion:** Analyze your results.  Which additive produced the largest bubbles? _____
How do you know?

_____

*TCR 8185 STEM*

# Reflections—Bubble Solution Investigation

1. What was your question about the bubble solution?

   _____

   _____

2. What was your hypothesis?

   _____

   _____

3. How did you test your hypothesis?

   _____

   _____

4. What were your results?

   _____

   _____

5. What did you learn from this experiment?

   _____

   _____

6. What was the hardest part?

   _____

   _____

7. What was your favorite part?

   _____

   _____

8. What surprised you the most?

   _____

   _____

# Mystery Mix

## Objectives

Students will observe simple chemical reactions and the properties of the matter involved and then give evidence to show how they know a chemical change has occurred. Then, the students will mix "mystery" substances (to make a bouncy ball), observe the properties of the substances before and after mixing and write about the chemical change.

## STEM Focus

*Physical Science:* Measurements of a variety of properties can be used to identify materials. When two or more different substances are mixed, a new substance with different properties may be formed.

*Science Inquiry:* Conduct an investigation to determine whether the mixing of two or more substances results in new substances.

*Science and Engineering Practices:* Plan and carry out investigations; analyze and interpret data; construct explanations; engage in argument from evidence.

*Crosscutting Concepts:* Cause and effect; energy and matter; stability and change

### Setup For Mini Challenge

▶ Prepare the materials for each group to perform the tests according to the directions on *Reaction Action*.

▶ Prepare the popping candy and soda demonstration. Stretch the neck of the balloon, and pour the popping candy into it, using a funnel. Place the balloon onto the mouth of the bottle. The top of the balloon should drop and hang over the bottle's side with the candy in it. When you are ready for the demonstration, just lift the balloon up so that the popping candy falls into the soda. *Note:* The reaction will create $CO_2$, which will inflate the balloon. It will probably not inflate all the way—just enough so students can observe the change.

### Setup For Main Challenge

▶ Prepare the borax solution. Mix ½ cup warm water with 1 tablespoon powdered borax.

▶ Students should not be told what the substances in this mix are until they are finished. Half fill cups of glue or cover the labels on glue bottles and label them *Substance 1*. Label the cups with cornstarch *Substance 2* and the cups with borax and water *Substance 3*.

▶ *Tip:* Students should mix using chopsticks or craft sticks. Coffee stirrers are not strong enough.

## Materials

### Mini Challenge

- *Reaction Action* (pages 64–67)
- Pop Rocks® candy (one packet)

| | |
|---|---|
| • baking soda | • lemon juice |
| • balloon | • soda in bottle |
| • clear cups | • vegetable oil |
| • craft sticks | • vinegar |
| • dish soap | • water |
| • food coloring | • whole milk |
| • funnel | |

### Main Challenge

- *Mystery Mix* (pages 68–69)
- *Polymer Chains and Cross-Links* (page 63)
- *Reflections—Mystery Mix* (page 70)
- borax and water
- bowls of soapy water
- chopsticks or craft sticks
- cornstarch
- cups (6–8 oz.)
- food coloring (optional)
- 1 tablespoon measure for each student
- ½ teaspoon measure for teacher
- paper plates
- timer
- white glue

## Time Frame

The Introduction and Mini Challenge will take 45 minutes.

The Main Challenge should take about 40 minutes.

Follow up with the Writing Reflection as time allows.

## Vocabulary

chemical change
physical change
chemical reaction

| | |
|---|---|
| conductivity | precipitate |
| evidence | properties |
| matter | substance |

# Mystery Mix

## Introduction

1. Ask students to describe **matter**. (*Anything that has mass and takes up space.*) Everything we see, touch, and interact with every day is matter. A **substance** is matter of a particular kind, such as *water*, *salt*, or *air*.

✏ Write the words *matter* and *substance* and their definitions on the board.

2. As part of this challenge, students will observe and describe the **properties** of matter.

✏ As a class, brainstorm different properties of matter that can be observed, such as *color*, *hardness*, or *shape*, and write them on a board or a chart.

3. Point out that there are some properties of matter that we need to use equipment to observe, such as temperature or weight, and others that we can only observe when we perform an action on the material, such as boiling point or **conductivity** (*whether electricity will travel through it*).

4. Let students know that they will be focusing on four easily observable properties of matter: *color*, *texture*, *odor*, and *state of matter* (solid, liquid, or gas).

### Explain the Science

Two ways that matter can change are through physical and chemical changes.

→ **Physical changes** can change the appearance or form of matter, but it is still the same matter. For example, cutting a piece of paper changes the paper, but it is still paper. Water can be in the form of ice, liquid water, or steam, but all of the forms are still water.

→ **Chemical changes** turn one kind of matter into a different kind of matter. If you burn paper, it isn't paper any more—it turns into ash, heat, light, and smoke. The molecules of the paper have been rearranged to make something different.

If you mix flour, water, egg, and sugar and bake it, it changes into cake. The molecules of the different ingredients have been changed into new material by heat.

5. Tell students that they will be looking for chemical changes called **chemical reactions** in this activity. They will observe and record the properties of matter before and after to determine if a chemical change has taken place. Ask:

—What might be some **evidence** that a chemical change has taken place? After some discussion, share the following examples if needed:

| Evidence of a Chemical Reaction | | |
|---|---|---|
| color change | → | apple turning brown |
| release of energy as heat or light | → | burning candle, fireworks, fire, explosion |
| formation of a gas | → | bubbles in soda |
| formation of a solid (*precipitate*) | → | cottage cheese |

Explain that a **precipitate** is a solid created by mixing liquids.

6. Mention that throughout this challenge, they will be observing and recording the properties of substances, creating chemical reactions, and observing and recording the changes that take place along with evidence of chemical reactions.

# Mystery Mix

## Mini Challenge

### Part 1–Reaction Action

1. Tell students that they will observe some different reactions and talk about the changes that occur.

2. Distribute a copy of *Reaction Action* to each student. Explain that they will perform tests 2, 3, and 4 as a group, but then each student will record his or her own observations.

3. Present *Test 1: Pop Rocks in Soda Demonstration* to students. Together, discuss the properties of the substances and have students record their observations of these substances on their recording sheets before mixing.

4. Perform the "popping candy" in soda demonstration for students. (See Setup.) Have students record their observations of the properties after the substances have been mixed. Ask:

   —Do you think a chemical reaction occurred? If they think that it has, ask them to describe their evidence.

   (*The gas that filled the balloon is evidence that a chemical reaction has taken place.*)

   —How do you know that the gas was produced if you can't see it?

   (*It fills the balloon.*)

5. Let students know that the gas created is carbon dioxide ($CO_2$).

### Part 2–Mixing It Up

1. Tell students that it is time to perform their own tests. Impress upon them that they will be acting as scientists, so they need to work neatly and carefully, following all safety directions.

2. Distribute the following materials to each group, each in a clearly labeled cup:

   | | |
   |---|---|
   | 1 tablespoon vinegar | ¼ cup water |
   | 1 tablespoon baking soda | food coloring |
   | dish soap—1 drop | ¼ cup whole milk |
   | ¼ cup vegetable oil | ¼ cup lemon juice |

3. Go over the directions for *Tests 2, 3, and 4* on the *Reaction Action* recording sheets as a class and answer any questions.

4. Have students perform the tests by following the directions for each test. Circulate to observe, assist as necessary, and remind students of safety procedures.

5. After all groups have finished testing and recording, come back together as a class and have groups share the observations and evidence. Discuss any discrepancies and what may have caused them. (*If a group gets results different from other groups, it is most likely that incorrect procedures were followed.*)

6. Here are the expected answers to *Reaction Action*:

   **Test 1:** Yes, a chemical reaction occurred. The evidence is the gas that inflated the balloon.

   **Test 2:** Yes. The evidence is that gas bubbles (*foam*) formed.

   **Test 3:** No. There is no evidence of a chemical reaction.

   **Test 4:** Yes. The evidence is the precipitate (*curdled milk*).

# Mystery Mix

## Main Challenge

### Define the Problem • Discuss Safety • Prepare

1. Tell students that, in the Main Challenge, they will observe the properties of some mystery substances and then mix them and look for a chemical reaction. Their hands may get sticky at first, but the end result should be worth it!

> **While this seems like a messy project, the amount of material involved is small. Having each student work over a paper plate will help minimize the mess, as will having a bowl or a plastic tub of soapy water on each table in which students can drop dirty utensils. Students will definitely need to wash their hands after making their bouncy balls, and you don't want a mad rush to the sink, so be prepared with a set procedure for hand washing.**

2. Provide each student with an 8-ounce cup, a mixing stick, a paper plate, and a copy of *Mystery Mix*.

3. Distribute the following shared materials to each table:
   - one plastic cup with about a cup of cornstarch, labeled *Substance 1*
     (You will need a tablespoon for each participant.)
   - a cup of glue labeled *Substance 2*
   - tablespoon-sized measuring spoons
   - a bowl or plastic tub of soapy water and paper towels or other hand wipes

4. Have students prepare their "lab" by placing their empty cup on their paper plate. Let students know that they are acting as scientists and need to work as neatly and carefully as possible. Because they don't know what the substances are that they will be working with, they also need to work cautiously and safely and listen carefully to all directions.

### Observe & Record

#### Substances 1 & 2

1. Have students measure 1 tablespoon of *Substance 1* (cornstarch) and put it in their cups. Remind students that, in science, accurate measurements are important. Show them how to use their stir sticks to level off the cornstarch in the measuring spoon before pouring it into their cups.

2. Have students observe *Substance 1*. Let them know that it is okay to touch the substance by dipping just the tip of their finger in and rubbing their fingers together to feel the texture. (No tasting!)

✏ Allow time for students to describe *Substance 1* on their recording sheets.

3. Have students measure 1 tablespoon of *Substance 2* and pour it into their cups on top of *Substance 1* —wait, don't stir yet! Then, have them observe the substance. They will probably know that it is glue—that's ok, but they still need to describe its properties. Again, it is okay to dip a finger in to feel the texture, but just a tiny bit!

✏ Allow time for students to describe *Substance 2* on their recording sheets.

4. If you are using food coloring, have students add a couple of drops to their cups.

# Mystery Mix

## Main Challenge

### Observe & Record (cont.)

**Substance 3**

1. Go around the room and show students *Substance 3* (the borax mixture) in a clear cup. Let them know that they may not touch it, or taste it, but they may look at it and record the other properties.

2. Show students how to smell *Substance 3* using a wafting technique by waving a hand over the cup towards their noses.

**Borax at concentrated strengths is a skin irritant, but when diluted properly is safe to touch. It should not be ingested, so make *no tasting* a major safety rule for this project! Students should wash their hands thoroughly after making and playing with their bouncy balls.**

3. Add ½ teaspoon of *Substance 3* to each student's cup. Tell them to let it sit for about 20 seconds and observe.

4. Have students stir carefully with a chopstick or a craft stick. When it gets too difficult to stir, students should scoop the mixture out and mold it with their hands.

5. *Teacher Tip:* Direct students NOT to pull it like taffy or slime. Instead, they should squeeze it a bit and then roll it around between their palms until it forms a ball.

6. Have students observe and record the properties of the new substance in their charts.

### Analyze & Evaluate

1. Discuss the properties of the new substance. Encourage students to talk about what changed in the properties of the substances and whether the changes could be reversed.

2. Give students time to complete the rest of the page.

3. Ask students to share some observations from their bouncy-ball experience.

4. If appropriate, share the information on page 63, *Polymer Chains and Cross-Links,* with students.

### Writing Reflection

✏ Have students complete the *Reflections—Mystery Mix* writing reflection individually.

### Extensions

Have students design experiments to test some questions about how bouncy balls are made.
→ Do different glues make better bouncy balls?
→ How does changing the amount of each ingredient change how the ball turns out?

# Polymer Chains and Cross-Links

## Explain the Science

➔ The glue contains a polymer that is made of small chains of molecules. These chains can easily move past each other, which gives glue the characteristics of a liquid.

**glue polymer chains**

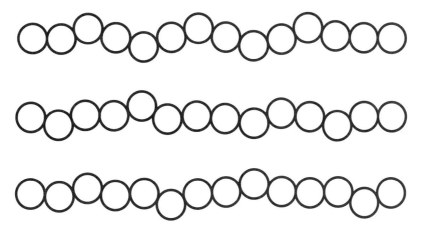

➔ When you add boric acid (*borax*), it causes the short strands to stick together and make long strands of molecules called *elastomers*.

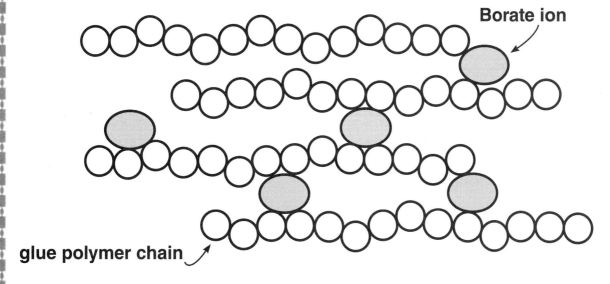

**Borate ion**

**glue polymer chain**

➔ The cornstarch helps hold everything together.
➔ The bouncy-ball polymers stay bonded together, but because their chains are long, they can bend and stretch, making it bouncy.

Name _____     Date _____

# Reaction Action

## Test 1: Pop Rocks in Soda Demonstration

Directions

1. Describe the properties of each substance in the chart below in the **Before** column.

2. Observe the demonstration.

3. In the **After** column, describe the properties of the substance created by mixing.

4. Answer the questions below the chart. State whether you think a reaction has occurred, and provide evidence.

| Properties | Before Mixing | After Mixing |
|---|---|---|
| Color | Popping candy: <br><br> Soda: | |
| Texture | Popping candy: <br><br> Soda: | |
| Odor | Popping candy: <br><br> Soda: | |
| State of Matter (solid, liquid, gas) | Popping candy: <br><br> Soda: | |

Did a reaction take place?     **Yes     No**

What is your evidence? _____

_____

Name _____     Date _____

# Reaction Action

## Test 2: Dish Soap, Baking Soda, and Vinegar

### Directions

1. Describe the properties of each substance in the chart below in the **Before** column.
2. Set the cup of baking soda on a plate.
3. Pour the dish soap into the baking soda, and mix gently.
4. Pour the vinegar in and watch.
5. In the **After** column, describe the properties of the substance created by mixing.
6. Answer the questions below the chart. State whether you think a reaction has occurred, and provide evidence.

| Properties | Before | After |
|---|---|---|
| **Color** | Baking soda | |
| | Dish soap | |
| | Vinegar | |
| **Texture** | Baking soda | |
| | Dish soap | |
| | Vinegar | |
| **Odor** | Baking soda | |
| | Dish soap | |
| | Vinegar | |
| **State of Matter (solid, liquid, gas)** | Baking soda | |
| | Dish soap | |
| | Vinegar | |

Did a reaction take place?      **Yes**      **No**

What is your evidence? _____

Name _____     Date _____

# Reaction Action

## Test 3:  Oil and Water

### Directions

1. In the **Before** column, describe the properties of each substance in the chart below.

2. In the **After** column, describe the properties of the substance created by mixing.

3. Answer the questions below the chart.  State whether you think a reaction has occurred, and provide evidence.

| Properties | Before | | After |
|---|---|---|---|
| Color | Oil | | |
| | Water | | |
| Texture | Oil | | |
| | Water | | |
| Odor | Oil | | |
| | Water | | |
| State of Matter (solid, liquid, gas) | Oil | | |
| | Water | | |

Did a reaction take place?     **Yes**     **No**

What is your evidence? _____

_____

*TCR 8185 STEM*                                         ©*Teacher Created Resources*

Name _____     Date _____

# Reaction Action

## Test 4: Milk and Lemon Juice

**Directions**

1. In the **Before** column, describe the properties of each substance in the chart below.

2. In the **After** column, describe the properties of the substance created by mixing.

3. Answer the questions below the chart. State whether you think a reaction has occurred, and provide evidence.

| Properties | Before | | After |
|---|---|---|---|
| Color | Milk | | |
| | Lemon Juice | | |
| Texture | Milk | | |
| | Lemon Juice | | |
| Odor | Milk | | |
| | Lemon Juice | | |
| State of Matter (solid, liquid, gas) | Milk | | |
| | Lemon Juice | | |

Did a reaction take place?     **Yes     No**

What is your evidence? _____

_____

Name _____     Date _____

# Mystery Mix

1. **Observe** the properties of each substance. **DO NOT TASTE.** To observe odor, use the wafting technique—don't stick your nose in it!

2. **Record** the properties of each substance in the **Before Mixing** column.

| Properties | Before Mixing | After Mixing |
|---|---|---|
| **Color** | Substance 1: | |
| | Substance 2: | |
| | Substance 3: | |
| **Texture** | Substance 1: | |
| | Substance 2: | |
| | Substance 3: | |
| **Odor** | Substance 1: | |
| | Substance 2: | |
| | Substance 3: | |
| **State of Matter** (solid, liquid, gas) | Substance 1: | |
| | Substance 2: | |
| | Substance 3: | |

Name _____     Date _____

# Mystery Mix (cont.)

3. **Predict** what will happen when you mix the substances.

_____

_____

4. Once the substances are all in your cup, observe them without mixing for about 20 seconds.

5. Then, mix with your stirring stick. Keep mixing until the substance gets too hard to mix any further and a lump forms in your cup.

6. After you have mixed, **observe** and **record** the new substance's properties in the **After Mixing** column of the chart.

7. Take the lump out with your hands, and roll it in between your palms to make a ball. It will be sticky at first but will firm up as you continue rolling and squeezing it.

8. **Describe** what changed.

_____

_____

9. Do you think a chemical reaction occurred?     **Yes     No**

_____

_____

What is your evidence?

_____

_____

10. Test your bouncy ball.

Does it bounce better on soft surfaces or hard surfaces?     **Soft     Hard**

What surface was the best for bouncing the ball?

**floor   pavement   carpet   other:** _____

How high will it bounce? _____

Name _____     Date _____

# Reflections—Mystery Mix

1. What was your favorite chemical reaction?

   _____

   _____

   Why?

   _____

   _____

2. Why do you think it is so important to work carefully when doing an experiment?

   _____

   _____

3. Describe the properties of your bouncy ball.

   _____

   _____

4. What did you learn from this challenge?

   _____

   _____

5. What was the hardest part?

   _____

   _____

6. What was your favorite part?

   _____

   _____

*TCR 8185 STEM*     *©Teacher Created Resources*

# Marble Mayhem

## Objectives

Students will learn about gravitational potential and kinetic energy through a hands-on investigation using marbles and then build gravity-powered marble "roller coasters."

## STEM Focus

*Physical Science:* The gravitational force of Earth acting on an object near Earth's surface pulls that object toward the planet's center.

*Engineering Design:* Define a simple design problem reflecting a need or a want that includes specified criteria for success and constraints on materials, time, or cost. Plan and carry out fair tests in which variables are controlled and failure points are considered to identify aspects of a model or prototype that can be improved.

*Science and Engineering Practices:* Plan and carry out investigations; analyze and interpret data; construct explanations and design solutions; engage in argument from evidence.

*Crosscutting Concepts:* Patterns; cause and effect; energy and matter

## Setup

### For Mini Challenge

▶ Prepare copies of *Marble Run Test* for each group.

▶ Each group will need space near a wall or other vertical surface. Students will place the pipe insulation track up against a vertical surface at different heights to test the height of the hill on which to start their marble run. They will need about 6 feet of space in front of the vertical surface to place their runs.

▶ See page 72 for directions and materials needed to make pipe-insulation test tracks.

▶ Set up one test track for demonstration. You will need half of one 6-foot length of ¾-inch pipe insulation, masking tape, cardboard, a marble, and perhaps a heavy book or a similar weight. You will also need a bucket or a box for the end of the ramp.

### For Main Challenge

▶ It's up to you how much time, space, and materials you have to let students work on their roller coasters. You can choose to let them build across and on top of desks, chairs, etc., or just on a flat surface.

▶ Use building materials you have on hand for this challenge.

## Materials

### Introduction and Mini Challenge

- *How to Make a Test Track* (page 72)
- *Marble Run Test* (page 79)
- bucket or box
- cardboard or foam core board
- marbles, 1 per group
- masking tape
- one half (lengthwise) of a 6-foot piece of ¾-inch pipe insulation per group
- pre-made test track (See page 72.)
- two tennis balls or other small, bouncy balls
- yardstick

### Main Challenge

- *Marble Coaster* (page 80)
- *Reflections—Marble Coaster* (page 81)
- building materials (See page 72.)

## Time Frame

The Introduction and Mini Challenge can be completed in one class session of about 40 minutes.

The Main Challenge can be completed in about 60 minutes, but the more time you allow, the more complex students can make their roller coasters.

Follow up with the Writing Reflection as time allows.

## Vocabulary

energy
force
gravitational potential energy
gravity
kinetic energy
mechanical energy
potential energy
transitions

# How to Make a Test Track

## Materials

- ¾-inch pipe insulation; half a 6-foot length per group
- masking tape
- cardboard
- heavy book or other weight

- marbles
- scissors
- bucket or box

## Preparation

Each group will need half of one 6-foot length of ¾" pipe insulation found at home improvement stores for under $2 per 6-foot piece. The pieces are already pre-cut lengthwise on one side.

1. Cut down the opposite side of each piece to split it in half lengthwise.

2. Prepare one 6-foot, half-piece for each group for the mini challenge, and several additional pieces for each group for the main challenge—the actual number will depend on your budget.

3. Set up one test track for the Mini Challenge demonstration.

## Making the Test Track

1. Bend one end of a 6-foot piece of track into a hill, and tape it down to a piece of cardboard or foam core. You will need an extra set of hands for this.

2. The hill should be 8 inches high in the middle and about 13 inches wide at the bottom.

3. Attach (or rest) the top of the track on the wall or another vertical surface.

## Tips

1. Keep the tape on the sides of the track and out of the channel as much as possible so it doesn't slow the marble down.

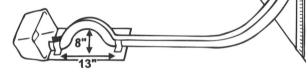

2. You may need to weigh down the cardboard during the test if you are working on a bare floor—anything small and heavy will do, such as a thick book or a canned good.

3. Place a box or a bucket on its side at the end of the track to catch the marble.

Reminder

**Students will be placing the pipe-insulation track up against a vertical surface at different heights to test the height of the hill on which to start their marble run. They will need about six feet of space in front of the vertical surface to place their runs.**

## Building Materials for Main Challenge

*Things to make tracks:* more pipe insulation, pool noodles (*split down the middle*), paper-towel tubes and toilet tissue tubes, funnels, paper plates, cut-apart cereal boxes

*Things that provide structure or support:* craft sticks, straws, pipe cleaners, cardboard, cardstock or index cards, milk cartons, plastic bottles, plastic or paper cups

*Building supplies:* scissors, masking tape, string, rubber bands, staplers

*TCR 8185 STEM* ©*Teacher Created Resources*

# Marble Mayhem

## Introduction

### Part 1

1. Review with students what they know about energy. Ask:

   —What is **energy**? (*The ability to do work.*)

✏️ Write the word *energy* and its definition on the board.

2. Explain that energy never disappears—it just changes from one form to another.

   **Examples**

   → A lightbulb converts electricity into light and heat.
   → A car converts energy from gasoline into motion.
   → A plant converts energy from the sun into energy that helps the plant grow.
   → Our bodies convert energy from food into energy that allows us to grow, live, and move.

3. Tell students that today, they will learn more about **mechanical energy**—the energy of moving things. There are two kinds of mechanical energy:

   **Potential energy** is stored energy.

   **Kinetic energy** is energy from motion.

✏️ Write *potential energy* and *kinetic energy* and the definitions on the board.

4. Ask students what force pulls down on everything around us all the time. (*gravity*)

   A **force** is a push or a pull.

   **Gravity** is a force that *pulls* toward the center of Earth.

5. Demonstrate potential energy and kinetic energy as they relate to gravity. Hold a pencil or another small object out in front of you. Ask:

   —Why does this pencil have potential energy? (*Because gravity is pulling on it.*)

6. Drop the pencil and ask:

   —What kind of energy did the pencil have when it dropped? (*Kinetic energy*)

7. Explain that because gravity pulls things down, it can cause them to have potential energy, which we call **gravitational potential energy**. Ask:

   —Can you name some things that have gravitational potential energy?

   **Examples**

   → A toy car at the top of a hill has gravitational potential energy. As it rolls down the hill the potential energy is converted to kinetic energy.
   → A book sitting on the edge of a table has gravitational potential energy. If it falls off the table, it has kinetic energy.

✏️ Write *gravitational potential energy* and its definition on the board.

# Marble Mayhem

## Introduction *(cont.)*

### Part 2

1. Pick up a tennis ball or another small ball that will bounce and hold it out in front of you. Ask:

   —How did this ball get its potential energy? (*I used my energy to pick it up.*)

> ## Explain the Science
>
> An object's *gravitational potential energy* is equal to the amount of work used to lift it. So, the higher we lift the object, the more potential energy it will have, and this potential energy can be converted into kinetic energy.

2. Hold up two balls, one high and one lower. Ask:

   —Which ball has more gravitational potential energy? (*the higher one*)

   —When I drop them, which one will have more kinetic energy? (*the higher one*)

3. Explain that *more kinetic energy* doesn't mean that something will fall faster, but it does mean that it will hit harder!

4. Drop both balls, and have students watch to see which one bounces higher. Ask:

   —Which ball bounced higher? (*The ball held higher will bounce higher.*)

   —Why did the ball that was held higher bounce higher? (*It had more gravitational potential energy, so it had more kinetic energy when it hit the ground. It hit harder, which made it bounce higher.*)

5. Explain to students that in this challenge, they will use the kinetic energy of a marble to propel it through a roller-coaster track.

# Marble Mayhem

## Mini Challenge

### Part 1

1. Show students a piece of the pipe insulation that has been split in half lengthwise. Tell them that this will be the track for their marble coasters. Demonstrate how a marble fits into the channel in the track. Ask:

   —How can I get the marble to roll along the track? (*Students may say that you should push it. Push the marble with your finger in the track. They may say that you should tilt the track. Tilt the track so that the marble runs along the channel.*)

2. Point out that when you lift one end of the track, you need to use energy to lift the marble up to the top. Then, when you put the marble in the track, its gravitational potential energy turns to kinetic energy as it rolls down the track.

3. Show students the prepared test track. Place the test track near a wall or another vertical surface (bookcase, filing cabinet, etc.) so that the free end rests on the wall. Set the start of the track less than one foot up the wall. Place a box, a bin, or a bucket on its side at the end of the track to keep the marble from rolling away. Ask students:

   —What will happen when I put the marble in at the beginning of the track? Let them discuss their predictions with a partner.

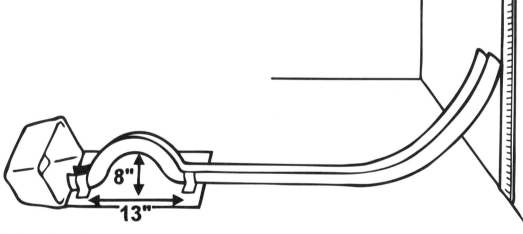

4. Carefully release the marble at the very top of the track, and let everyone watch what happens. (*The marble will not make it over the hill.*) Ask:

   —Does the marble need more or less energy to go over the hill? (*more*)

   —How can we give it more energy? (*Raise the height of the start.*)

5. Raise the start as high as you can get it to go. You will need to move the cardboard (supporting the hill) closer to the wall. Ask:

   —What happens to the marble? (*The marble went too fast and jumped out of the track near the top of the hill.*)

# Marble Mayhem

## Mini Challenge

### Part 2

1. Tell students that they are now going to build their own tracks to find the best height to get the marble to go over the hill.

2. Distribute a copy of *Marble Run Test* to each group of three or four students along with a length of track, a marble, some masking tape, a piece of cardboard, and a yardstick.

3. Go over the test sheet with students and make sure that they understand the procedures. Point out that, when building their roller coasters, students will have to adjust the height of their start and experiment with each feature they build to make the marble run smoothly through the whole coaster.

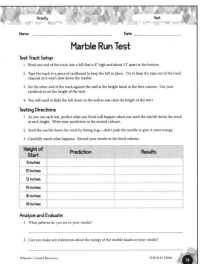

4. Have them decide how they will determine whose turn it is to release the marble on each run. Tell students that it is important that they release the marbles without pushing them so that the *only* energy they have is from gravity.

5. Circulate while students build their tracks and perform their tests to ensure that they are following the procedures and recording their data.

6. Bring the class back together, and discuss the results. For each row in the chart, have one group share its results.

   → If other groups got the same, or almost the same, result, they should raise their hands.

   → If any group got a wildly different result, have them share it, and the class should discuss what might have caused any discrepancies.

7. Have groups share their answers to the last two questions.

## Explain the Science

Students will most likely notice that the higher the start, the faster the marble moves. This is because lifting the marble higher gives it more *potential energy,* which is converted to *kinetic energy* as it rolls downhill.

- If they start the marble at a low point, it won't have very much energy and it won't go over the hill.

- If they start it up too high, it will have too much energy and it will move too fast, causing it to jump out of the track.

# Marble Mayhem

## Main Challenge

### Define the Problem and Plan

1. Tell students that they will now use what they learned to build a marble roller coaster.

2. Show students the materials available for this challenge. Have the class brainstorm some ways to use different items in a marble roller coaster.

### Possibilities

- The outside of a paper plate can create a curved track for taking a marble around corners.
- Paper-towel rolls can be used to make tunnels.
- Items such as cups, milk cartons, and plastic bottles can be used as supports for the track.

3. Tell students to be careful about **transitions** (*changes*) from one piece of track to another or from one material to another—the transitions need to be as smooth as possible so the marble can roll through.

4. Go over the constraints for this challenge. The constraints tell engineers what they can and can't do.

5. Write the Challenge Constraints and the Criteria for Success for the *Marble Mayhem* challenge on the board or chart paper, or make copies for students to refer to throughout the challenge. Add any other constraints as they pertain to your situation, such as *Don't tape the track to any of the furniture.*

## Challenge Constraints

☼ Build a marble roller coaster powered only by gravity.

☼ Create a fun ending where the marble is stopped safely in an interesting way.

☼ Use only the materials given. You do not have to use all of the materials.

☼ **Criteria for Success:** The marble safely rolls all the way to the end of the roller coaster.

6. Give a copy of *Marble Coaster* to each group. Read through it together, and answer any questions.

7. Have students gather building materials. Allow groups time to handle the materials, discuss, brainstorm, and plan their coasters.

# Marble Mayhem

## Main Challenge

### Build • Test • Improve

1. Review the *Engineering Design Process* (page 14) with students. Remind them that they can test, improve, and retest as much as they like in the time available. Their goal is to get their coaster working so that the marble rolls all the way through to the end.

2. Students will need to test frequently so that they can see if they need to adjust the height of the start or any of the components. Let them know how much time they will have.

3. Circulate as students build and test their coasters to observe and question for formative evaluation.

4. Give students some warning as they reach the end of the testing time so they can wrap up.

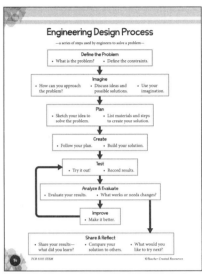

### Analyze & Evaluate

1. Ask each group to demonstrate their roller coaster for the class. Have them explain each feature of their roller coaster and any improvements or discoveries that they made.

2. If time allows, let the groups try each other's roller coasters. Caution students not to break anything!

### Writing Reflection

✎ Have each student complete the *Reflections—Marble Mayhem* writing reflection individually.

### Extension

Challenge students to create new roller coasters using tennis balls instead of marbles. Which roller coaster was faster?

Name _____    Date _____

# Marble Run Test

## Test Track Setup

1. Bend one end of the track into a hill that is 8 inches high and about 13 inches apart at the bottom.

2. Tape the track to a piece of cardboard to keep the hill in place.  Try to keep the tape out of the track channel so that it won't slow down the marble.

3. Set the other end of the track against the wall at the height listed in the first column.  Use your yardstick to set the height of the start.

4. You will need to slide the hill closer to the wall as you raise the height of the start.

## Testing Directions

1. As you run each test, predict what you think will happen when you send the marble down the track at each height.  Write your prediction in the second column.

2. Send the marble down the track by letting it go—don't push the marble to give it extra energy.

3. Carefully watch what happens.  Record your results in the third column.

| Height of Start | Prediction | Results |
|---|---|---|
| 8 inches | | |
| 10 inches | | |
| 12 inches | | |
| 14 inches | | |
| 16 inches | | |
| 18 inches | | |

## Analyze and Evaluate

1. What patterns do you see in your results?

_____

2. Can you make any statements about the energy of the marble based on your results?

_____

Name _____    Date _____

# Marble Coaster

**Directions:** Plan a marble roller coaster powered only by gravity.

1. Look through the available materials and brainstorm ideas for hills, turns, loops, or other features of roller coasters. Sketch some ideas for different features.

2. Think about how you will connect the different features and in what order to make sure the marble keeps moving until the end. Write ideas here.

_____

_____

3. How will you end your roller coaster in an interesting way that stops the marble safely?

_____

_____

4. Sketch the plan for your roller coaster on a separate sheet of paper. Label all the parts. You may have to move some things around as you build—that's okay! This sketch will give you a place to start.

5. Build your marble roller coaster!

## Building Tips

- To keep the marble moving downhill, place the tallest features at the beginning of the coaster and work your way down to the shortest features at the end.

- Transitions between pieces of track should be as smooth as possible.

- Try to keep the track clear of tape so the marble can keep moving.

- Test, test, test! Run the marble every time you change or add something and make adjustments as you go along.

TCR 8185 STEM

Name _____     Date _____

# Reflections—Marble Coaster

1. Draw and label a diagram of your final roller coaster.

2. What materials did you use?

   _____  _____  _____

   _____  _____  _____

3. How did you adjust or improve your coaster?

   _____

   _____

4. What discoveries did you make as you were building and testing your roller coaster?

   _____

   _____

5. What did you learn about gravity?

   _____

   _____

6. What was the hardest part of the challenge?

   _____

7. What was your favorite part of the challenge?

   _____

# Tallest Towers

## Objectives

Students will learn about the center of gravity through a hands-on activity. Students will then use what they have learned to build towers using only one material, with the goal of building the tallest tower possible. Students will use the Engineering Design Process to improve their designs, build, and test to create taller towers.

## STEM Focus

*Physical Science:* The gravitational force of Earth acting on an object near Earth's surface pulls that object toward the planet's center.

*Engineering Design:* Generate and compare multiple possible solutions to a problem based on how well each is likely to meet the criteria and constraints of the problem. Plan and carry out fair tests in which variables are controlled and failure points are considered to identify aspects of a model or prototype that can be improved.

*Science and Engineering Practices:* Use mathematics and computational thinking; construct explanations and design solutions; engage in argument from evidence.

*Crosscutting Concepts:* Cause and effect; scale, proportion, and quantity

## Setup

Do the Introduction and Mini Challenge on the first day, and have students choose their material for the Main Challenge. Then, you will have a better idea of how many different materials you will need for the building day.

### For Mini Challenge

▶ Gather empty aluminum cans and cups for each student or pair. Additionally, provide ½-cup measuring cups for each group.

▶ Prepare work areas that can get wet, and have towels or paper towels available.

### For Main Challenge

▶ Gather the materials for building. Each group will choose one material (and will need quite a lot).

#### Suggestions

* paper cups     * paper plates     * newspaper
* cardboard      * index cards      * plastic water bottles

▶ Students should build their towers on the floor—not on the carpet. Spread groups around the room so that they don't knock over one another's towers.

▶ Take pictures or videos of the building process.

## Materials

### Introduction and Mini Challenge

- aluminum cans
- bottle of glue with sealed tip
- ½-cup measuring cups
- paper cups
- towels or paper towels
- water

### Main Challenge

- *Tallest Towers* (page 89)
- *Reflections—Tallest Towers* (page 90)
- camera (optional)
- materials for building (See Setup.)
- measuring tapes
- paper or plastic cups
- scissors

## Time Frame

The Introduction and Mini Challenge can be completed in one class session of about 40 minutes.

The Main Challenge can be completed in 45 minutes to an hour.

Follow up with the Writing Reflection as time allows.

## Vocabulary

base
center of gravity
foundation
height
rotate
stable
tower
unstable

# Tallest Towers

## Introduction

1. Have a few students stand with their backs against a wall so that both heels are touching the wall. Place a pencil about 1½ feet in front of them. Ask students to predict whether they will be able to lean over and pick up the pencil without moving their feet or bending their knees.

2. Have students try to pick up the pencils. Discuss what happened. Ask:

   —Why couldn't they lean forward?

   —Did they automatically put one foot out or put a hand down? Why?

   —What force is making them fall over? (*gravity*)

3. Let all students try this demonstration.

4. Tell students that one of the reasons they couldn't reach the pencil was because of their center of gravity. Ask:

   —What do you know about the term **center of gravity**? (*The center of gravity of an object is the point at which weight is evenly dispersed, and all sides are in balance.*)

✎ Write the term *center of gravity* and its definition on the board.

### Part 2

1. Have students stand on one foot, holding their standing leg straight. Ask:

   —If someone gave you a little push on your shoulder, do you think you might fall over? (*yes*)

2. Have students stand on both feet, keeping their feet together and their legs straight. Ask:

   —Does standing this way feel more **stable** (*unlikely to topple over or give way*)?

   —Would you fall if given a little push? (*maybe*)

3. Have students stand with their feet spread apart. Ask:

   —Does this position feel more stable? (*yes*)

   —If someone gave you a little push, would you fall? (*probably not*)

### Explain the Science

An object becomes unstable when its center of gravity moves outside of its **base**. Tell students that their center of gravity is somewhere around their belly button in the center of their torso—the exact location is slightly different for each person. When they leaned over, their center of gravity moved away from their feet (their base) so they fell over. Normally, if they leaned over to pick up a pencil, they would either shift their weight backward, or they would put one foot out so that the center of gravity stayed in the middle, and they wouldn't fall over.

# Tallest Towers

## Mini Challenge

### Part 1

1. Challenge students to use what they have learned about the center of gravity in order to balance an aluminum can on its edge. (*They need to think about the center of gravity of the can and its contents.*)

2. Give each student or pair of students an empty aluminum soda can. Let them try balancing the can for a little while.

3. Share this diagram with students. Ask:

   —Where is the center of gravity when the can is empty? (*Be sure students understand that the center of gravity is in the middle of the can, not on the outside. Ask students to explain this instead of just pointing it out.*)

   —What happens when you try to balance an empty can? (*The center of gravity moves outside of the base, and it falls over.*)

   —How could you move the center of gravity? (*Add liquid—you may have to suggest this after a time.*)

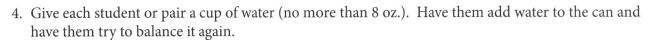

4. Give each student or pair a cup of water (no more than 8 oz.). Have them add water to the can and have them try to balance it again.

   Some students might be able to balance the can if they get the amount of water just right. The optimal amount of liquid in the can is 100 ml (just under ½ cup). Keep towels handy for any spills!

5. Show students the following diagram and tell them to try ½ cup of water in the can. If it won't quite balance, they should pour out just a little of the water until it does.

6. Once students have successfully balanced a can, challenge them to give it a gentle push to make it **rotate** (*move in a circular motion around an axis*). Ask students:

   —Where is the center of gravity in the can? (*Over the point where the can is touching the table.*)

   —How does this allow the can to move in a circle? (*The center of gravity stays over the same point as it rotates.*)

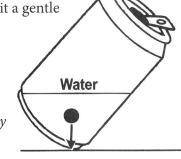

**If students are having difficulty or do not believe this balancing act can be done, consider showing a short video after significant attempts have been made. Search for phrases like "balancing a soda can and rotating" or "how to balance a soda can," and, as always, preview before sharing!**

# Tallest Towers

## Mini Challenge *(cont.)*

### Part 2

1. Remind students of their standing/balancing activity. Ask students:

   —Would you consider the balanced cans to be stable? (*No!*)

   —Why not? (*The balanced cans would definitely be classified as* **unstable** *since it would be very easy to knock them over.*)

2. Place a book flat down on a table and ask:

   —Is the book stable? (*Yes*)

   —How do you know? (*It would be impossible to knock the book over.*)

   —Can you point out some other objects in the room that are stable and not likely to fall over without someone making a significant effort? (*desk, chair, etc.*)

3. Point to the flat book again. Ask:

   —What if I stacked another book on top of this one? Would they be stable? (*Yes*)

   —Can I keep stacking books forever and keep them stable? (*No*) Why not? (*Because the center of gravity would keep moving up, making the tower less and less stable, and eventually, it would fall over.*)

4. As a further demonstration, try to balance a sealed bottle of glue on its tip, and then try to balance it right side up on its base. Ask:

   —Why is the bottle more stable on the flat end than on the tip? (*The tip is very small, so it's difficult for the center of gravity to stay within it. The base is wider, so the center of gravity stays within it.*)

5. Have a discussion about the differences observed between things that are stable and things that are unstable. Ask:

   —What helps make things stable?

## Explain the Science

Lead students to see that a larger **foundation**, or base, helps an object be more stable than a smaller foundation. An object will tip over when the center of gravity lies outside the supporting base of the object. A larger foundation gives more area for the center of gravity to stay inside. Objects that are larger or heavier toward the bottom have a lower center of gravity and are thus more difficult to tip over. Say, "Let's keep this in mind when we are building towers in the Main Challenge."

# Tallest Towers

## Main Challenge

### Define the Problem

1. Tell students that, in the Main Challenge, they will build towers and will use what they have just experienced to help make their own towers stable. Ask students:

   —What is a **tower**? Discuss. (*Mention that a tower is a structure that is taller than it is wide.*)

2. As a demonstration, build a tower by stacking single cups alternately right side up and upside down on top of each other. Keep building until the tower falls. It's okay to pretend to be clumsy and stack the cups so that they fall easily. Students love outdoing the teacher!

3. Challenge students to think about how they could use what they know about the center of gravity to build a more stable tower that will be taller than yours.

4. Place students in groups of three to five. Give each group a copy of the *Tallest Towers* recording sheet and assign each group a tower-building area.

5. Go over the *Challenge Constraints* and *Criteria for Success* for this challenge.

✎ Write the constraints on the board or chart paper, and go over them with students.

---

## Challenge Constraints

⚙ Use only one building material.

⚙ No tape, glue, or other connectors allowed!

⚙ Use the chosen material any way you want. You may cut, roll, or fold it.

⚙ Build on the floor or ground so that you can reach the top of your tower.

⚙ If your tower falls before you can measure it, build it again.

⚙ **Criteria for Success:** To succeed, your tower must stand on its own long enough to be measured.

---

6. Demonstrate how to use a measuring tape to measure **height**. Decide together if students will measure in feet and inches or meters and centimeters.

7. Remind students that they will have to be very careful while measuring so that they don't knock over their towers. Caution them to also be very careful as they move about the room so that they don't knock over another group's tower.

8. Tell students that accidental bumps are bound to happen. Be supportive, even if one member has an "oops" moment. Take student suggestions for what they could say if someone accidentally knocks down a tower, such as, *That's okay—let's build it again!* or *Oops! Let's build it again.*

9. Go over the *Engineering Design Process* (page 14) with students.

**During design and testing, failure is an expected part of the engineering process. Engineers use failures to see what went wrong and to improve their designs so that, when they build the real thing, it won't fail. Let students know that they can learn from what went wrong and can try again.**

# Tallest Towers

## Main Challenge *(cont.)*

### Imagine • Plan • Create

1. Show students the available materials. Give them a set amount of time to discuss how they might use each material to build a tower.

2. Encourage students to be creative and to try lots of different ways to build with just one material. Remind them that they can manipulate the material any way they want.

3. If a group is struggling, show them how to make a small cut in two pieces of cardboard or another material and slot them together.

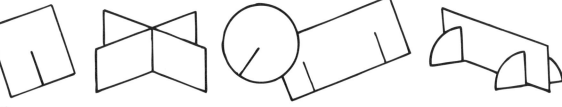

**You will be surprised at how inventive students can be when given the restriction of only using one material. Cutting slots into materials and pushing them together, rolling and folding materials into columns or beams—there are many ways to make this work! If all groups choose paper cups (it does seem to be the easiest material) you might want to do a random draw for materials or have students repeat the challenge while using a different material.**

4. When time is up, have each group state which material they have selected.

5. Give groups time to discuss and sketch their first tower design.

✏ Sketches should be quick and simple without too much detail.

6. Encourage students to think about what they learned in the Mini Challenge about what happens when a center of gravity gets too high up or goes off to one side.

✏ Ask students to put an *X* on their sketch where they think the center of gravity will be.

7. Remind students that, if they think they have a good tower, they should measure it before it falls! They can always add to it and measure again.

✏ Record all measurements on the *Tallest Towers* recording sheet.

**You might have groups that build towers higher than they can reach. If possible, provide step stools or stable chairs for them to stand on and, review safety precautions.**

8. Try to take photos and/or video of students working.

# Tallest Towers

## Main Challenge (cont.)

### Test & Improve

1. As students are working, circulate to observe, and prompt with questions as needed. For example, you might ask:

   —How did you use what you know about the center of gravity?

   —What did you change in your design after your last tower fell?

✐ Be sure that they are recording the height of each tower before they move on to a new design and that they are sketching each design before building.

2. If groups use up all of their available material in a successful tower, challenge them to try a different design. If they used a lot of their material for the foundation of their tower, suggest that, maybe, they could try a slightly smaller foundation so that they have more material for height.

3. Once students have built and measured a successful tower, encourage them to build another tower with a different design or with different materials.

4. Give students a few minutes' warning before time is up. Tell them that the tower that they are now building will be their last.

5. Once time is up, tell all groups to measure their last tower if it is still standing.

✐ Give students a couple of minutes to record the tower's height and to add other information to their recording sheets.

### Analyze & Evaluate

1. Graphing will help students visualize the data to see how their towers compare to others.

✐ Have each group graph the heights of its towers. Students will need to fill in the *y*-axis with either feet/inches or meters/centimeters.

2. Have each group share their sketches and graphs and have them report on which of their towers was the tallest. Ask them to explain why they think that a particular tower design was most successful.

3. Ask each group what changes it made in its tower designs that helped make the towers taller. Encourage students to cite evidence for their answers, such as: *In our first tower, the foundation was only one foot wide. When we made it wider the tower went higher because the center of gravity stayed in the middle.*

### Writing Reflection

✐ Have each student complete the *Reflections—Tallest Towers* writing reflection individually.

### Extensions

- Have students select a different material and have them use it to build another tower. Each material has different properties and will present a different challenge.

- Offer some new materials, and allow one connecter. Some good combinations: straws and paper clips, toothpicks and gumdrops, uncooked spaghetti and mini-marshmallows, balloons, and tape.

- Make the challenge harder by moving the center of gravity higher. Have students build towers that hold an object at the top (golf or tennis ball, small cup with pennies or washers in it, or a textbook).

Name _____    Date _____

# Tallest Towers

1. What one material did you choose to build your tower?

_____

2. Sketch your idea for a tower in the **Tower 1** box.

3. Put an *X* where you think the center of gravity will be.

4. Build your tower.  If it falls, build it again!  Once you think your tower is ready, measure it with a measuring tape. Be careful!

5. Record the height on your sketch.

6. Once you have built a successful tower, improve your design and build and test other towers!  Sketch them below.

Tower 1   height: _____

Tower 2   height: _____

Tower 3   height: _____

Tower 4   height: _____

7. Graph the heights of your towers below.

| Height | Tower 1 | Tower 2 | Tower 3 | Tower 4 |
|--------|---------|---------|---------|---------|
|        |         |         |         |         |

Name _____     Date _____

# Reflections—Tallest Towers

1. What was the challenge?

   _____

   _____

2. What material did your group choose?  Why?

   _____

   _____

3. Was your first tower stable?     **Yes**     **No**

4. What adjustments did you make to your first tower?

   _____

   _____

5. In the box to the right, sketch your most successful tower.

6. How high was it?

   _____

7. Why do you think that this tower was the most successful?

_____

_____

What is your evidence?

_____

_____

8. What would you do differently?

_____

_____

# Water Filtration

## Objectives

Students will learn about water filtration and will test different water filtering materials. Then, they will design, build, and test a water filter.

## STEM Focus

*Earth Science:* Human activities in agriculture, industry, and everyday life have had major effects on the land, vegetation, streams, ocean, air, and even outer space. But individuals and communities are doing things to help protect Earth's resources and environments.

*Engineering Design:* Plan and carry out fair tests in which variables are controlled and failure points are considered to identify aspects of a model or a prototype that can be improved. Engineers improve existing technologies or develop new ones to increase their benefits, decrease known risks, and meet societal demands.

*Science and Engineering Practices:* Design solutions and construct explanations; engage in argument from evidence.

*Crosscutting Concepts:* Systems and system models; cause and effect; structure and function

## Setup

### For the Mini Challenge

▶ Prepare the "dirty" water in a large bucket, using the directions on page 92.

▶ Designate a sink or another large bucket for students to use to discard water.

▶ Find clear, plastic cups (four per group) that are flexible enough to poke holes in without cracking.

### For the Main Challenge

▶ Gather a wide variety of additional filtration materials, including five more clear, flexible cups per group. See the suggested list on page 92.

▶ Fill in the *Budget and Shopping List* with the available materials. See page 92 for detailed instructions.

## Materials

### Introduction and Mini Challenge

- *Saltwater vs. Freshwater* (page 98)
- *Water Filter Materials Testing* (page 99)
- two 5-gallon buckets
- aquarium gravel
- clear, flexible plastic cups
- 1 cup purple, powdered-drink mix
- 1 tablespoon glitter
- twigs, leaves, bark
- play sand or rinsed beach sand
- pushpins
- water

### Main Challenge

- *Clean It Up!* (page 100)
- *Budget and Shopping List* (page 101)
- *Reflections—Water Filtration* (page 102)
- clear, flexible plastic cups
- "dirty" water (See page 92.)
- materials for filtering (See page 92.)
- measuring cups
- paper towels
- pushpins
- stopwatch or timer

## Time Frame

The Introduction and Mini Challenge will take about 45 minutes.

The Main Challenge will take approximately 45–60 minutes.

Follow up with Writing Reflection as time allows.

## Vocabulary

| | |
|---|---|
| filter | pollution |
| manmade | prime |
| natural | toxins |

# Water Filtration

## Mini Challenge–Preparation and Materials

1. Prepare the "dirty" water in a 5-gallon bucket by combining the following:

   - 4 gallons of water

   - 1 cup purple, powdered-drink mix

   - 1 tablespoon fine glitter

   - a couple of handfuls of twigs, leaves, and bark cut into small pieces

2. Gather the water and the filter materials for each group to make a filter.

   - four pushpins

   - ¼ cup play sand or rinsed beach sand

   - ¼ cup aquarium gravel

   - 2 cups of "dirty" water

   - 2 cups of clean water

   - 3 clear, flexible plastic cups

> **Note:** The cups must be the flexible variety so that students can poke holes in them without causing cracks in the plastic.

## Main Challenge–Preparation and Materials

1. Fill in the *Budget and Shopping List* with the available materials.

   → Keep prices between $1 and $5.

   → Price the more obviously useful materials, such as sponges and coffee filters, higher than less obvious items, such as marbles or feathers.

   → The recommended total budget is $10, but adjust as needed.

   → Indicate the number or amount of each item for the price, e.g., 10 marbles for $2 or 1 sponge for $5.

   → You may also put a limit on the number or amount of some materials if supplies are limited.

2. Gather materials to be used to create filtration systems in clear, plastic cups.

---
### Suggestions

| | | |
|---|---|---|
| * aquarium gravel | * fabric pieces | * paper napkins |
| * beach sand (rinsed) | * fake fur | * paper towels |
| * cheesecloth | * feathers | * pebbles |
| * coffee filters | * gauze | * play sand (clean) |
| * cotton balls | * marbles | * sponges |
| * egg cartons | * muffin liners | * toilet paper |

---

# Water Filtration

## Introduction

1. Introduce the topic of **water filtration** by asking the following question and have students share their ideas with a partner (turn and talk or think-pair-share) and then share with the class. Ask students:

   —What percentage of the water on Earth is freshwater that we can use?

2. Then, share the *Saltwater vs. Freshwater* information sheet, and discuss it as a class.

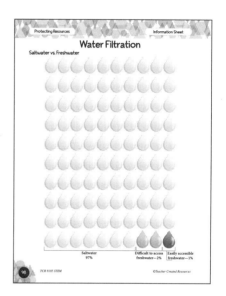

3. Together, make a list on the board of all the ways that humans use water (*drinking, bathing, cooking, cleaning, industry, farming, raising livestock, etc.*).

4. Impress upon students that there is little water available for all these human needs, so we need to use it wisely.

5. Ask students the following questions and add their responses to the board:

   —What is the definition of the word **pollution**? (*If necessary, provide this definition: Harmful substances released into the environment.*)

   —What pollutants could be in our water that would make it unfit to use? (*dirt, animal waste, human waste, trash, chemicals, bacteria, **toxins** [poison or harmful chemicals], etc.*)

6. With students, circle or highlight the pollutants on the list that can be **manmade** and underline those that can be **natural**. Keep in mind that some pollutants, such as animal waste and bacteria, can be both natural and manmade. (*Lead students to see that both natural and human factors can pollute water.*) Ask students:

   —How could you remove these things from water? (*Boil them, filter them, or add chemicals such as chlorine to the water.*)

7. Tell students that the water that comes from their taps or that they get in bottles is treated in multiple ways in order to ensure that it is clean and safe.

8. For this challenge, they will be filtering water to remove some pollutants, but ***they won't be able to produce water that is clean enough for human use.***

# Water Filtration

## Mini Challenge

1. Tell students that they will be building a water **filter** (*a device for removing particles or impurities*) and testing two of the possible filter materials—sand and gravel.

2. Divide students into groups. The number and size of each group is up to you.

3. Supply each group with the following:
   - *Water Filter Materials Testing* recording sheet
   - three 9 oz. clear, flexible plastic cups (larger cups will work)
   - four pushpins
   - ¼ cup play sand available in craft and art supply stores or beach sand (rinsed)
   - ¼ cup aquarium gravel
   - 2 cups of "dirty" water
   - 2 cups of clean water

4. Designate a sink or bucket for students to use to discard water.

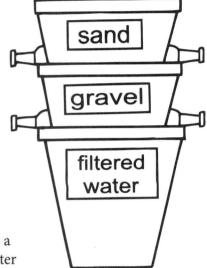

## Build the Filter

1. **Cups 1 & 2**—Have students *carefully* use the pushpins to poke about a dozen holes in the bottoms of two of the cups. These will be the filter cups. Tell students to spread the holes out around the bottom of the cup.

2. Then, show them how to put the pushpins into the sides of the filter cups so that they will stack on top of each other. (See diagram.)

3. **Cup 3**—The third cup should remain as is (*no holes*) and be placed under the filter cups to collect the samples.

4. Instruct students to put the sand into one filter cup and the gravel into the other.

5. Have them run ½ cup clean water through each filter cup to **prime** (*prepare*) it. The water should rinse out any dust and prepare the filter for the dirty-water tests. Discard the water used for priming.

## Materials Testing

After each test, students will look carefully at the filtered water in the bottom cup and draw and describe what they see on their recording sheets. They should discard the filtered water after each test.

1. First, have students run ½ cup of prepared dirty water through each filter separately and record observations.

2. Next, run dirty water through the filters stacked with the sand first (top cup), and the gravel cup (underneath) and record observations.

3. Finally, run dirty water through the filters stacked with the gravel first (top cup), and the sand cup (underneath) and record observations.

4. As a class, discuss the results:
   —What filter or combination of filters produced the cleanest water?
   —Why do you think that your filter or combination of filters worked best?
   —Was there any difference in whether the water went through the sand first or the gravel first?

# Water Filtration

## Main Challenge

1. Tell students that their challenge is to build a water-filtration system that makes water as clear as possible. Emphasize that the water will not be clean enough to drink, even if it looks clean, because they are not disinfecting the water to remove bacteria and are not going to test for toxins.

2. Distribute copies of the *Clean It Up!* recording sheet and the *Budget and Shopping List* to each group. Go over the recording sheet and the budget sheet together.

✏ Have students enter the budget amount on both pages.

3. Show students the "dirty" water that they will use in the challenge. Explain that the list of "pollutants" (glitter and natural materials) in the "dirty" water is on their recording sheets. All groups will take their samples from the same container of water to make sure that the challenge is fair to all.

4. Go over the Challenge Constraints and Criteria for Success for this challenge. The constraints tell the engineers what they can and can't do, and the criteria for success details the goal of the challenge. The Constraints and Criteria are repeated for students on the *Clean It Up* recording sheet.

## Challenge Constraints

⚙ Build a water filter by using the available materials.

⚙ Your budget for purchasing materials is $ _____.

⚙ Prices of materials are listed on your project sheet.

⚙ Your filter may have up to three layers (cups).

⚙ You may combine materials within each layer any way you want.

⚙ The bottom cup will catch and hold the filtered water.

⚙ Before the final test, you will be allowed to run clean water through your filter in order to prepare it.

## Criteria for Success

⚙ Your filter must clean 1 cup of water within 2 minutes.

⚙ Your cup of filtered water should be as clear as possible.

⚙ Filtered water samples from all groups will be compared at the end of the challenge.

# Water Filtration

## Main Challenge *(cont.)*

1. Provide students with the following items at no cost:

   - a measuring cup

   - five flexible, clear plastic cups

   - six pushpins

2. Let them know that three of the cups are for them to create filters. The fourth cup is to catch the filtered water, and the fifth cup is to transport the dirty water from the class container to their workspace.

3. Show students the available materials. Let them handle the materials and let them brainstorm ways to use them. Remind them that they cannot spend more than their budget. They might want to think ahead to plan for alternative materials if their first choices do not work as well as anticipated.

✐ Give students time to sketch their filters and to fill out the first part of their recording sheets.

4. Supervise students as they "purchase" materials. Check to be sure their budget sheets are completed accurately.

5. Review the *Engineering Design Process* (page 14) with students. Remind them that they can test, improve, and retest as much as they like in the time available.

6. Tell them how much time they have to complete their filters and advise them that you will give a five-minute warning to complete the challenge.

### Create • Test • Improve

1. Have students gather their materials and give them ample time to build their water filters according to their plans and sketches.

2. Circulate as students work on their filters. Observe and ask questions for formative assessment, such as:

   —How did you choose the materials for this challenge?

   —How will your filter remove each type of pollutant?

3. Remind students to prime their filters by running clean water through them before testing. Point out that once they test their filter by pouring dirty water through it, they may need to rinse or replace some of the materials in the filter before testing again.

# Water Filtration

## Main Challenge *(cont.)*

### Create • Test • Improve *(cont.)*

4. Once students are ready for their final test, have them run clean water through their filter again and then discard the water.

5. Use a stopwatch or a timer to ensure that the water goes through their filters in under two minutes.

6. Have them label a clean cup with their names and then have them pour one cup of dirty water through their filter into the cup.

7. Save the final, cleaned water for each group for a comparison later.

✏ Remind students to write their results on the *Clean It Up!* recording sheets.

### Analyze & Evaluate

1. Have each group describe how they built their water filter and how it worked. They should share their process for testing and any improvements they made as well.

2. Line all of the final samples up to do a comparison. Determine which sample or samples appear to be the cleanest.

3. Have a class discussion about the water filters created and any patterns students noticed. For example, they may have observed that one particular material was good at catching larger particles while another was good at removing smaller particles or that they were able to remove the blue coloring (*it was absorbed by the sand*) but not the red coloring.

4. If time allows, have groups improve their filters based on what they learned from the class discussion and retest.

### Writing Reflection

✏ Have each student complete the *Reflections—Water Filtration* writing reflection individually.

### Extensions

- Have students research how water is treated in their own community.

- Research human impacts on your local water supply and the positive and negative effects they have on plants and animals. Consider the following questions:

  —Why do these impacts exist?

  —What is the advantage to humans?

  —Have students research ways that they can help reduce human impact on the environment, such as picking up litter, recycling, and saving water. Make posters to share these positive behaviors with your school.

# Saltwater vs. Freshwater

Saltwater
97%

Difficult to access
freshwater–2%

Easily accessible
freshwater–1%

TCR 8185 STEM

Name _____     Date _____

# Water Filter Materials Testing

## Directions

1.  Run ½ cup of dirty water through each filter and combination of filters, A–D.

2.  Draw and describe the resulting filtered water for each test in the cups below.

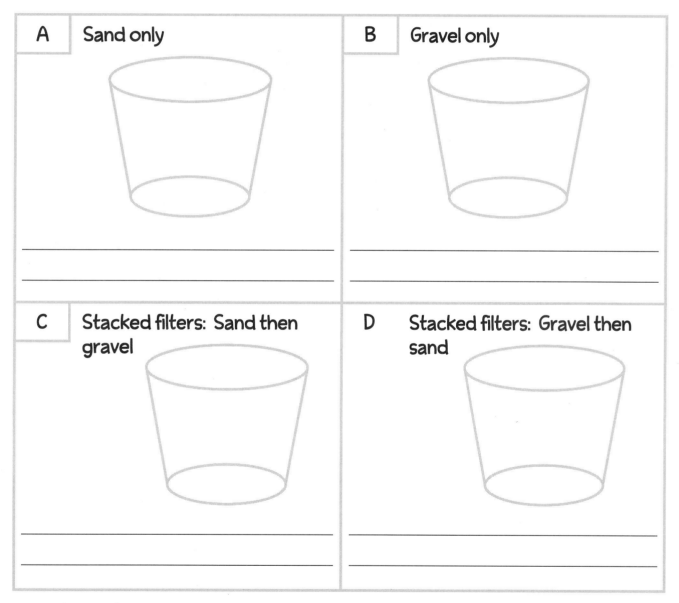

| A | Sand only |
| B | Gravel only |
| C | Stacked filters: Sand then gravel |
| D | Stacked filters: Gravel then sand |

3.  What conclusions can you make from the results?

_____

_____

Name _____    Date _____

# Clean It Up!

## Challenge Constraints

⚙ Build a water filter using the available materials.

⚙ Your budget for purchasing materials is $_____.
    Prices of materials are listed on the *Budget and Shopping List.*

⚙ Your filter may have up to three layers (cups). You may combine materials within each layer any way you want.

⚙ The bottom cup will catch and hold the filtered water.

⚙ Before the final test, you will be allowed to run clean water through your filter to prepare it.

## Criteria for Success

⚙ Your filter must clean 1 cup of water within 2 minutes.

⚙ Your cup of filtered water should be as clear as possible.

⚙ Filtered water samples from all groups will be compared.

## Directions

1. On a separate paper, draw a diagram of your planned filter, and label the materials.

2. Fill out the *Budget and Shopping List* for your group. **Reminder:** Do not spend more than your budget! After testing, you may want to put new filter materials in some of your layers. Don't forget to think about that when shopping!

3. Prime your filter with clean water before testing and between each test.

4. During testing, pay attention to how long it takes for water to go through your filter. Your final filter must run at least one cup of water through within two minutes.

5. Draw and describe the water sample in your final test.

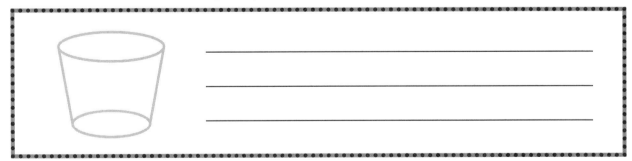

6. Was your filter able to remove some or all of the pollutants?    Some    All
   If some, which ones?

_____

# Budget and Shopping List

## Directions

1. Enter the materials you will use in Column 1.
2. Enter the price of each item in Column 2.
3. Enter how many of each item you will purchase in Column 3.
4. Enter the total cost of each item in the last column.
5. Add up all purchases, and enter the total cost at the bottom.

**Your total budget is**

$ _____.

| Material | Price | Quantity Purchased | Cost |
|---|---|---|---|
| measuring cup | free | | |
| 5 cups | free | | |
| 6 pushpins | free | | |
| | | | |
| | | | |
| | | | |
| | | | |
| | | | |
| | | | |
| | | | |
| | | | |
| | | | |
| | | | |
| | | | |
| | | | |
| | | | |
| | | | |
| | | | |
| | | | |
| | | Total Cost: | |

Name _____     Date _____

# Reflections—Water Filtration

1. Did you have to change your original idea as you were testing?     **Yes     No**

   How? _____

   _____

   _____

2. Did your filter completely remove the pollutants?     **Yes     No**

   Why do you think you got this result? _____

   _____

3. If you were to do this challenge again, what would you do differently?

   _____

   _____

4. What part of creating your water filter was the hardest?

   _____

   Why?_____

   _____

5. What part of creating your water filter was the most fun?

   _____

   Why?_____

6. What was the most surprising thing you learned about fresh water?

   _____

   _____

7. What is something you think you can do to prevent water pollution?

   _____

   _____

# Green Roofs: Soak It Up!

## Objectives

Students will test the absorbency of different materials. Then, they will design and build a model of a green roof that holds as much water as possible.

## STEM Focus

*Earth Science:* Human activities in agriculture, industry, and everyday life have had major effects on the land, vegetation, streams, ocean, air, and even outer space. But individuals and communities are doing things to help protect Earth's resources and environments.

*Engineering Design:* Define a simple design problem reflecting a need or a want that includes specified criteria for success and constraints on materials, time, or cost. Generate and compare multiple possible solutions to a problem based on how well each is likely to meet the criteria and constraints of the problem.

*Science and Engineering Practices:* Develop and use models; analyze and interpret data; use mathematics and computation; construct explanations and design solutions.

*Crosscutting Concepts:* Scale, proportion, and quantity; systems and system models; structure and function

## Setup

### For Mini Challenge

▶ Set up bowls or pie tins of water for each group.

▶ Gather materials for testing. Some should be absorbent, some permeable, and some waterproof.

#### Suggestions

| | | |
|---|---|---|
| * cardboard | * mulch | * plastic wrap |
| * cotton balls | * newspaper | * potting soil |
| * foil | * paper towels | * sponges |
| * gravel/pebbles | * pipe cleaners | * vermiculite |
| * marbles | * plastic bags | * wax paper |

### For Main Challenge

▶ Prepare squares of foam core or cardboard, five at 6-inches square and one at 7-inches square for each student group.

▶ Purchase or gather plants (available at garden centers). Any dense, low-growing plant will work, particularly sedums or short grasses.

▶ Have water and measuring cups available at each tray.

## Materials

### Introduction and Mini Challenge

- *Green Roof Layers* (page 108)
- *Green Roof Materials Test* (page 109)
- access to water
- bowls or pie tins
- materials for testing (See Setup.)

### Main Challenge

- *Green Roof Models* (page 110)
- *Reflections—Green Roofs: Soak it Up!* (page 111)
- materials for building (See Setup.)
- foam core or cardboard (See Setup.)
- duct tape
- potting soil or other growing medium
- sod or other low-growing plants
- timers
- deep trays or plastic bins
- measuring cups or graduated cylinders
- water

## Time Frame

The Introduction and Mini Challenge can be completed in one class session of about 45 minutes.

The Main Challenge can be completed in about an hour, but allow more time if students are really absorbed in the activity.

Follow up with the Writing Reflection as time allows.

## Vocabulary

| | |
|---|---|
| absorbent | runoff |
| green roof | storm water |
| permeable | waterproof |
| pollutant | |

Name _____   Date _____

# Green Roofs: Soak It Up

## Introduction

1. Write the phrase ***storm water runoff*** on the board and discuss what the term means. (*Explain that, when it rains, some water is absorbed into the ground and some is not. The water that is not absorbed runs downhill and eventually ends up in a body of water.*)

✏ Add this definition to the board: *Storm water runoff is storm water that flows over the surface of the land and downhill towards streams, rivers, lakes, and the ocean.*

2. Discuss the last time it rained, and have students share their knowledge and experiences. Ask:
   —Did they see any water runoff?
   —Where did they see it?
   —In which direction was it flowing?
   —What was it running over?
   —What problems might be caused by storm water runoff? (*pollutants, flooding, mudslides*)

### Explain the Science

Explain that, as runoff makes its way across the land, it can pick up **pollutants**, such as fertilizers, pesticides, motor oil, and pet waste. The water carries these pollutants into streams, lakes, rivers, and the ocean.

Runoff is a particular problem in cities because surfaces like concrete and asphalt are **waterproof**, meaning water does not absorb into them—but runs off. Water flows over these surfaces, picking up pollutants as it goes.

Natural materials such as soil and plants can absorb water and slow storm water runoff, but concrete and asphalt cannot.

3. Have students discuss this in their groups. Ask:
   —What are some possible ways to reduce storm water runoff?

4. Invite groups to share their ideas, and make a list on the board.

5. If students have not listed **green roofs,** add it to the list. Then ask:
   —Does anyone know what a green roof is, or has anyone seen one? (*Explain that roofs of buildings can be covered with a waterproof surface and then planted, creating a "living surface."*)
   —How could a green roof help reduce storm water runoff? (*The plants and soil could absorb rain and keep it from running off.*)

6. Continue the discussion and add that green roofs provide other benefits as well, such as:
   • regulating the temperature of a building so that less heating and cooling are needed
   • filtering pollutants and carbon dioxide out of the air
   • providing habitats for wildlife

7. Ask students what they think happens to the water that is absorbed by a green roof. (*The plants use the water, and it is returned to the air via transpiration [flow of water through a plant from roots to leaves] and evaporation [process of turning from liquid to vapor].*)

# Green Roofs: Soak It Up

## Mini Challenge

1. Explain to students that they will be designing and making models of green roofs and testing them for absorbency (how much water they can hold), but before they design these roofs, they will need to test various materials to see which ones will be the best ones to use in their designs.

2. Give each group a copy of *Green Roof Layers*. Read it together. Ask students to think about which materials they may want to use to build each layer of their model green roofs.

3. Caution students that when they select the materials to test, they should include some materials that they think will be **absorbent** (*able to hold water*), and some that may be **permeable** (*allowing water or gas to pass through*) or **waterproof** (*not allowing water to pass through.*)

✏ Add the words *absorbent*, *permeable*, and *waterproof* and their definitions to the board.

4. Show students the available materials, and provide ample time for them to handle and inspect them.

5. Each group should choose five materials to test. Make sure that each group tests some different materials so that as many materials as possible are being tested during the challenge. All groups will combine their data at the end of the Mini Challenge.

 **Remind students that they will need at least one material that is waterproof to keep the water from getting into the building and one material that is permeable for the filter layer.**

6. Provide each group a copy of the *Green Roof Materials Test* recording sheet. Go over it together, and answer any questions.

7. Provide each group with a bowl or a pie tin of water. Give students time to run their tests and record their data.

8. Compile all data from all the groups. Display a three-column chart with the headings *Absorbent, Permeable,* and *Waterproof*. Have each group list the materials they tested in the correct columns. Tell students that they may use this information to select materials for their model roofs.

| Absorbent | Permeable | Waterproof |
|---|---|---|
| able to hold water | allowing water or gas to pass through | not allowing water to pass through |
|  |  |  |

# Green Roofs: Soak It Up

## Main Challenge

### Define the Problem

1. Tell students that in this challenge, they will design and build models of green roofs by using the research results from the Mini Challenge.

2. Distribute a copy of *Green Roof Models* to each group. Read through it together, and answer any questions.

3. Go over the *Challenge Constraints* and *Criteria for Success* for this challenge. The constraints tell the engineers what they can and can't do, and the criteria for success details the goal of the challenge. Mention that they can find a copy of these constraints on their recording sheets.

---

### Challenge Constraints

⚙ Build a green roof model using available materials.

⚙ Your model should have all of these layers: waterproof membrane, drainage/storage layer, filter layer, growing medium, and plants.

⚙ Your model should hold as much water as possible.

⚙ **Criteria for Success:** To be successful, green roof models must hold at least 75% of the cup of water poured over them (or ¾ cup).

---

4. Review the *Engineering Design Process* (page 14) with students. Remind them that they can test, improve, and retest as much as they like in the time available. Let them know how much time they have.

*Teacher Note*

The roof models will be 6-inch squares, so if you can precut the plants to just under that size, it will make planting easier (and less messy). Most nursery plant trays are 11-inch by 22-inch so you can cut eight 5.5-inch by 5.5-inch mats from one tray.

### Imagine & Plan

1. Have each group assemble a model building by using duct tape to attach four 6-inch squares of foam core or cardboard to each other to form walls. A fifth 6-inch square can be the floor or base.

2. Add a 7-inch square to the top to form a roof, and duct-tape the edges of the roof to the walls. Explain to students that they will build their green roof on top of their model building.

3. Give students time to brainstorm ideas and to make a plan for their green roof models.

# Green Roofs: Soak It Up

## Main Challenge *(cont.)*

### Build • Test • Improve

1. Have students gather their materials and build their green roof models on top of their model buildings.

2. Circulate as students are working to observe and ask questions for formative evaluation, such as:

   —What materials are you using?

   —How does each material (*layer*) respond to water?

   —What will happen to the water as it hits each layer?

3. Have students test their green roof model by placing their model building in a tray or a plastic bin and pouring one cup of water slowly over the roof. After 10 seconds, they need to remove the model building from the testing tray.

4. Students should collect and measure the runoff by pouring the water from the testing tray into a measuring cup or a graduated cylinder.

5. Have students calculate the percentage of water that ended up in the testing tray as runoff. If necessary, assist students with the calculation.

   | | | | | | |
   |---|---|---|---|---|---|
   | ¼ cup = 25% | ⅓ cup = 33% | ½ cup = 50% | ⅔ cup = 66% | ¾ cup = 75% | 1 cup = 100% |

6. If a roof holds less than 75% of the water, students should reevaluate their roof and improve it, and then test again.

### Analyze & Evaluate

1. Bring the class together, and have each group give a short presentation about how they designed and built their green roof model. Ask them to share the following information:

   → which materials they used

   → how they came to their design decisions

   → how much water their most successful roof held

   → what, if any, improvements they made

2. Bring the class together to debrief. Talk about each roof design's strengths and weaknesses. Have students share ideas for improvements.

### Writing Reflection

✏ Have each student complete the *Reflections—Green Roofs: Soak it Up!* writing reflection individually.

### Extension

Have students research green roof designs. Which ones are their favorites? Are there any local to their hometown?

# Green Roof Layers

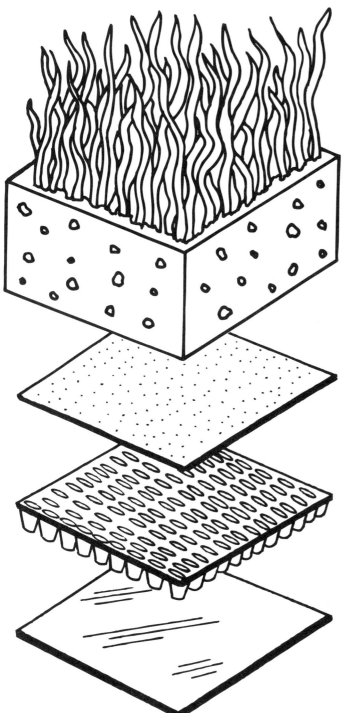

**Plants**—Plants need to grow close together and have shallow root systems

**Growing medium**—Soil or other material in which plants can grow

**Filter layer**—Allows water through (permeable) but keeps the soil from washing down into the lower layers

**Drainage/storage layer**—Absorbs water and slowly releases it back into the growing medium or into drains

**Waterproof membrane**—Keeps water from getting into the building

Name _____     Date _____

# Green Roof Materials Test

## Directions

1. List your materials in the first column.

2. In the second column, write your prediction for whether water will absorb into the material (*absorbent*), go through the material (*permeable*), or not affect the material (*waterproof*).

3. Dip an edge of each material approximately ¼-inch into the water.

4. Observe how the water affects each material.

5. Write your results in the third column.
   → If the water travels up into the material, the material is *absorbent*.
   → If the water goes through the material but does not travel up into it, the material is *permeable*.
   → If the water does not go through or travel up the material, the material is waterproof.

| Materials | Prediction | Result |
|-----------|-----------|--------|
|           |           |        |
|           |           |        |
|           |           |        |
|           |           |        |
|           |           |        |

Name _____     Date _____

# Green Roof Models

**Challenge:** Build a green roof model according to the Challenge Constraints.

## Challenge Constraints

- ⚙ Build a green roof model using available materials.
- ⚙ Your model should hold as much water as possible.
- ⚙ Your model should have all of these layers: waterproof membrane, drainage/storage layer, filter layer, growing medium, and plants.

   **Criteria for Success:** To be successful, green roof models must hold at least 75% of the one cup of water poured over them.

## Construction

1. Choose the materials for each layer of your green roof.

   Plants: _____

   Growing medium: _____

   Filter layer: _____

   Drainage/storage layer: _____

   Waterproof membrane: _____

2. Assemble your model building using the 6-inch and 7-inch squares and tape.

3. Sketch your green roof model and label each layer.

4. Build your green roof model on top of your model building.

## Test the Green Roof

1. Place the model in the testing tray.

2. Pour one cup of water slowly over your roof.

3. Wait 10 seconds, and remove your green roof model from the tray.

4. Pour any runoff water out of the testing tray into a measuring cup.

5. How much water ran off of your green roof model?

   → What percentage of the one cup of water ran off? _____

   → What percentage of the one cup of water was absorbed by your roof? _____

6. If your roof absorbed less than 75% of the water, what could you have done differently.

*TCR 8185 STEM*     ©*Teacher Created Resources*

Name _____    Date _____

# Reflections—Green Roofs: Soak It Up!

1. Draw and label the green roof layers your group created.

<br><br><br><br><br><br><br><br><br><br><br>

2. How did your group arrive at your final design? _____

_____

What decisions did you make? _____

_____

3. What percentage of the water did your final green roof model hold?

_____ %

4. What do you think went well?

_____

5. What was your favorite part?

_____

6. Which part was the hardest?

_____

7. What surprised you?

_____

# Next Generation Science Standards Correlation

| Challenge | Performance Expectations | Disciplinary Core Ideas | Science and Engineering Practices | Crosscutting Concepts |
|-----------|--------------------------|-------------------------|-----------------------------------|-----------------------|
| **Fun with Bernoulli** | 5-PS 1-1 3-5 ETS 1-1 3-5 ETS 1-3 | PS1.A | Ask questions and define problems; plan and carry out investigations; analyze and interpret data; use mathematics and computational thinking; construct explanations. | Cause and effect; energy and matter; scale, proportion, and quantity; stability and change |
| **Seed Growth Investigation** | 5-LS1-1 | LS1.C | Ask questions; plan and carry out investigations; analyze and interpret data; use mathematics and computational thinking; construct explanations | Energy and matter |
| **Break It Down** | 5-LS2-1 3-5-ETS1 3-5-ETS2 | LS2.A | Plan and carry out investigations; construct explanations and design solutions | Energy and matter; systems and system models |
| **The Bubble Solution Investigation** | 5-PS1-4 | PS1.B | Ask questions and define problems; plan and carry out investigations; analyze and interpret data; use mathematics and computational thinking; construct explanations | Cause and effect; energy and matter; scale, proportion; and quantity; stability and change |
| **Mystery Mix** | 5-PS1-4 | PS1.A PS1.B | Plan and carry out investigations; analyze and interpret data; construct explanations; engage in argument from evidence | Cause and effect, energy and matter; stability and change |
| **Marble Mayhem** | 5-PS2-1 3-5-ETS1 3-5-ETS3 | PS2.B | Plan and carry out investigations; analyze and interpret data; construct explanations and design solutions; engage in argument from evidence | Patterns; cause and effect; energy and matter |
| **Tallest Towers** | 3-5-ETS2 3-5-ETS3 | PS2.B | Use mathematics and computational thinking; construct explanations and design solutions; engage in argument from evidence | Cause and effect; scale, proportion, and quantity |
| **Water Filtration** | 5-ESS3-1 | ESS3.C | Design solutions and construct explanations; engage in argument from evidence | Systems and system models; cause and effect; structure and function |
| **Green Roof: Soak It Up** | 5-ESS3-1 3-5-ETS1 3-5-ETS2 | ESS3.C | Develop and use models; analyze and interpret data; use mathematics and computation; construct explanations and design solutions | Scale, proportion, and quantity; systems and system models; structure and function |

*TCR 8185 STEM*